Uniting Green Criminol and Earth Jurisprudenc

As planet Earth continues to absorb unprecedented levels of anthropogenically induced environmental and climatic change, two similar academic schools of thought have emerged in recent years, both making sustained efforts to explain how and why this state of affairs has evolved.

These two disciplines are known as *green criminology* and *earth jurisprudence*. Whilst these areas of study can be seen as sub-disciplines of their parent subjects, law and criminology, this book proposes that much can be achieved by authors uniting and collaborating on their academic work. By doing this, it is argued that green criminology stands to benefit from a discipline that places mother nature at the heart of lawmaking and therefore providing a solution to the environmental harms identified by green criminologists.

Furthermore, earth jurisprudence will profit from utilising the breadth of academic work produced within the green criminology academic arena. Therefore, this book seeks to unite green criminology and earth jurisprudence in an effort to find solutions to the extraordinary environmental problems that the world now faces.

Dr. Jack Lampkin is a Lecturer in Policing at Teesside University. He obtained his PhD in 2018 from the University of Lincoln's Law School and has several academic publications in the field of green criminology.

‘Combining the insights of green criminology and earth jurisprudence, this energising and thought-provoking book offers an invitation to think hard and act fast – a vital task for the times. It provides an intellectual gateway to understanding and responding to the environmental crises threatening our planet, thereby offering conceptual direction to struggles past, present and future.’

Professor Rob White, *University of Tasmania, Australia*

Uniting Green Criminology and Earth Jurisprudence

Jack Lampkin

LONDON AND NEW YORK

First published 2021
by Routledge
2 Park Square, Milton Park, Abingdon, Oxon OX14 4RN

and by Routledge
605 Third Avenue, New York, NY 10017

First issued in paperback 2022

Routledge is an imprint of the Taylor & Francis Group, an informa business

Publisher's Note
The publisher has gone to great lengths to ensure the quality of this reprint but points out that some imperfections in the original copies may be apparent.

British Library Cataloguing-in-Publication Data
A catalogue record for this book is available from the British Library

Library of Congress Cataloging-in-Publication Data
A catalog record for this book has been requested

ISBN 13: 978-0-367-61311-2 (pbk)
ISBN 13: 978-0-367-61306-8 (hbk)
ISBN 13: 978-1-003-10513-8 (ebk)

DOI: 10.4324/9781003105138

Typeset in Times New Roman
by Apex CoVantage, LLC

For Bethany

Contents

Tables

Foreword

The Earth faces environmental crises from many angles. Climate change and the chaos it will bring are already upon us and will worsen in the coming years. Pollution from plastics and from pesticides, fertilisers, insecticides, and so forth plagues the oceans and the soil. Our fellow non-human inhabitants are dying and being killed at an unprecedented rate. And further billions of non-humans live in abhorrent conditions and endure pain-filled, short lives. At the same time, a tiny proportion of humanity is richer in terms of wealth and material possessions than ever before. Corporations, too, have reached immense levels of wealth and power. Even 'everyday' people in the West and North consume at environmentally damaging levels. At the heart of this environmental devastation are societies centred on the (individual) human. Urgent changes and improvements are needed for both the planet and all those who live on it.

In step green criminology and earth jurisprudence. These radical, critical subfields of criminology and law challenge the human centeredness – anthropocentrism – of most of the world. And although they both emerged in the 1990s and champion quite similar beliefs, nearly no synthesis of the two environmentally minded subfields has been attempted. Thus, *Uniting Green Criminology and Earth Jurisprudence* is an exciting and valuable undertaking.

The book opens by setting the stage on the state of the environment. In particular, Jack focuses on deforestation, biodiversity loss, non-human animal use and abuse for food, and plastic pollution. All of these areas provide rich examples of harms that are mostly legal, and the examples highlight that the legal system supports and perpetuates environmental devastation. The fact that environmental harm and legality are often inextricably intertwined provides a solid foundation for why green criminology and earth jurisprudence should be united.

Jack then goes on to detail the historical and theoretical foundations of, first, green criminology and then earth jurisprudence. These chapters provide essential background information for both sub-fields and thus bring scholars from any discipline up to date on the foundations, differences, and commonalities of green criminology and earth jurisprudence. Chapter 4 makes a compelling case for the benefits and advantages to be gained by synthesising the two sub-fields. Combined concrete steps can be taken to transition to an earth-centred world that does not wreak havoc on the environment for short-term human gains.

In Chapter 5, Jack explores three unique real-world examples of where earth jurisprudence has been put into practice. These are powerful testaments to the possibilities for change presented by earth jurisprudence. Underpinned with the same eco-philosophies of much of green criminology, earth jurisprudence as a legal foundation for societies could transform their environmentally destructive ways.

In the conclusion, Jack makes the critical point that the focus of scholarship must be on solutions. And by synthesising green criminology and earth jurisprudence, this can happen through formulation of strategies to change society for the better. *Uniting Green Criminology and Earth Jurisprudence* is an excellent addition to two rapidly growing sub-fields and a valuable inspiration to move these areas of scholarship even further forward to help save the planet.

Dr Tanya Wyatt
Professor of Criminology
Northumbria University

Acknowledgements

There are many people to thank, for I could not have completed this book without the help and support of friends, family, and work colleagues.

Firstly, I must praise my beautiful wife, Beth, who is always there for me regardless of my endeavours. The love and support you give every day provided the backbone to this book.

The majority of this manuscript was written during the UK government's COVID-19 'lockdown' from March to May 2020. To my parents Sarah and Steve, my brother Ben, and my friends Matthew and Lauren Lowe, thank you for the calls, texts, and FaceTimes that kept me motivated during that difficult period of social isolation.

To my colleagues at Teesside University, of whom there are too many to mention, thank you for your encouragement during the writing of this book. In particular, my immediate team – Gareth Addidle, Lynsey Pinchen, Ruth McGrath, Helen Pepper, Samantha Scott, Cain Major, Kevin Baldam, and Maggie Leese – whose reassurance and encouragement I am incredibly grateful for.

To Professors Matthew Hall and Tanya Wyatt, thank you for introducing me to green criminology and providing me with the academic skills necessary to undertake this book.

Any errors or omissions in this work remain my own.

Abbreviations

ALLLA	Apollo Lunar Legacy Landing Act
CHF	Conventional Hydraulic Fracturing
GDP	Gross Domestic Product
GPGP	Great Pacific Garbage Patch
GPS	Global Positioning Systems
LRME	Law of the Rights of Mother Earth
NM	Nautical Miles
OST	Outer Space Treaty
REDD+	Reducing Emissions from Deforestation and Degradation
ToP	Treadmill of Production
UHF	Unconventional Hydraulic Fracturing
UK	United Kingdom
UNCOPUOS	United Nations Committee on the Peaceful Uses of Outer Space
US	United States

1 Introduction to issues of global environmental harm

> Extinction has always been a feature of life on Earth, but the domination of global ecosystems by people has caused a sharp rise in the rate of extinctions to far above prehuman levels. Loss of biodiversity affects the functioning of natural ecosystems and threatens human well-being.
>
> (Johnson et al., 2017: 270)

1.1. Introduction

The earth is changing. Environmental destruction is now occurring at such an unprecedented and exponential rate that it is now widely acknowledged that we (as humans) have induced a shift from the Holocene to the Anthropocene geological epoch (Lewis and Maslin, 2015; South, 2015). This means that humans are having such a profound impact on planet Earth that some of the damage is now irreversible. Typical examples of this include widespread species loss (He et al., 2018; Román-Palacios and Wiens, 2020), melting of the polar ice caps causing sea levels to rise (Gross, 2019), and human and non-human climate migration (a state whereby organisms must re-locate as their habitat becomes increasingly inhospitable and uninhabitable; Brisman et al., 2018; Westra, 2009).

The motivation for this book therefore is twofold. This first factor lies in the failure of legal systems to prevent catastrophic environmental harm. Humans have long known about the impact of their systems and societies on the global climate and ecology yet have been unsuccessful in preventing ecological damage using legal systems. In fact, it is widely acknowledged that legal systems continue to facilitate (rather than prevent) environmentally destructive practices, particularly those integral to the successes of large corporations and big businesses (Kramer, 2013; Stretesky et al., 2014).

The second motivation for this book concerns the long-term failings of both law and criminology to not only recognise the significance of their (lack of) involvement with environmental issues but also subsequently to provide credible, holistic solutions to what has now been described as an environmental crisis (Buell, 2003). The emerging fields of green criminology and earth jurisprudence have started to tackle these issues since the turn of the millennium, but authors and researchers within these fields have not yet collaborated to share and utilise their skills across disciplines, beside both fields claiming to be inclusive and multi-disciplinary (Schillmoller and Pelizzon, 2013: 7; South et al., 2013).

Therefore, the principle aim of this book is to unite the disciplines of green criminology and earth jurisprudence. It is hoped that discussing both disciplines in unison will encourage and foster collaboration; instigate the sharing of ideas and resources; engage scholars in important critical debate about prudent environmental and socio-legal issues; and start a conversation and dialogue between scholars in both areas. The premise is that doing so will be beneficial for both green criminology and earth jurisprudence, respectively.

Section 1.3. will discuss the structure and layout of this book in greater detail. However, the purpose of this opening chapter is to highlight the importance of future work within green criminology and earth jurisprudence. This will be done by outlining the current state of environmental harm and degradation directly induced by humans in Section 1.2. The point of this is to demonstrate the current failings of national and international law to instigate and enforce effective measures to curb and prevent environmental harm. Doing so will set a foundation for Chapters 2 (*green criminology*) and 3 (*earth jurisprudence*) that offer particular insights and solutions into this state of affairs.

1.2. The magnitude of sustained environmental destruction across planet earth: academic and scientific evidence that the earth is changing

In 1964 the United States (US) Surgeon General produced a landmark report highlighting evidence that regularly smoking tobacco leads to a number of health problems, including lung cancers and chronic bronchitis (Alberg et al., 2014; Chassin et al., 1990). This was the result of sustained research into the effects of cigarette smoking on public health beginning in the 1940s. However, prior to World War II, there was very little concern about smoking cigarettes. In fact, smoking was (and arguably sometimes still is) advertised as a healthy lifestyle choice (see: Amos, 1996: 81). As a result, it is fair to say that the human health impacts of smoking were unknown for a considerable amount of time.

The same, however, cannot be said of human knowledge of environmental damage caused as a direct result of human acts and production processes. It is not possible to identify exactly when humans began to recognise the impact that their lifestyles were having on the natural environment. However, Samaan (2011: 261) uses the work of the early Roman author Tertullianus (writing at roughly the turn of the second century AD), who realises that:

> All places are now accessible . . . cultivated fields have subdued forests; flocks and herds have expelled wild beasts. . . . Everywhere are houses, and inhabitants, and settled governments, and civilized life. What most frequently meets the view is our teeming population; our numbers are burdensome to the world . . . our wants grow more and more keen, and our complaints bitter in all mouths, whilst nature fails in affording us her usual sustenance.

This quote from Tertullianus shows us that the knowledge and understanding of human impacts on the environment are not necessarily a recent phenomenon. Foley and Lahr (2015: 1) also provide some important context on the sustained and long-standing human impact on the natural world when they denote that:

> Humans have had a major impact on the environment. This has been particularly intense in the last millennium but has been noticeable since the development of food production and the associated higher population densities in the last 10,000 years. The use of fire and overexploitation of large mammals has also been recognized as having an effect on the world's ecology, going back perhaps 100,000 years or more.

Despite this, it is now widely recognised that the environmental damage of the 21st century occurs at a much greater scale (in terms of the many types of environmental degradations, and the frequency and intensity of induced environmental harms) than at any point in previous human history. This state of affairs has been attributed to many things including (but not limited to) a considerable growth in the human population (Cohen, 2010); globalisation and significant advances in technology (Bu et al., 2016); the extraction and burning of natural resources (i.e. coal, oil, natural gas, timber, nuclear energy) contributing to increasing greenhouse gas emissions (Cohen, 2010); and the environmental degradation that is a necessary component to the capitalist political economy whereby mass consumption and the focus on economic growth are essential to capitalism's success (Dauvergne and Lister, 2011; Stretesky et al., 2014).

There is a plethora of academic and scientific research dedicated to identifying anthropocentrically generated environmental harm. However, it is impossible to discuss all of this excellent work in this chapter. Instead, I will identify and discuss the significance of a few key studies that accurately depict the current state of human-induced environmental degradation. In order to do this, I will draw upon four key case study areas: the continued mass deforestation of the earth's forests (Section 1.2.1.); the mass extinction of the earth's ecology and non-human species (Section 1.2.2.); the use, abuse, and consumption of animals to satisfy the Western human diet (Section 1.2.3.); and the pollution of the earth's oceans with plastics and other non-biodegradable matter (Section 1.2.4.). Doing this will enable us to see not just the extent of human impacts on the environment but the failings of governments and legal systems to adequately address these issues and protect the natural world. Doing this will highlight the importance of uniting green criminology and earth jurisprudence in the proceeding chapters of this book.

1.2.1. Mass and unrelenting global deforestation

Timber is big business. Essmann et al. (2007: 60) estimate that there are 5,000 commercial timber products 'mainly (consisting of) construction timber, furniture, paper and firewood (that) contributes to some 2 percent of the world GDP.' This demonstrates the extent of the connection between timber and human societies. Whilst timber is a renewable natural resource, it is slow growing. One of the fastest-growing tree species in the world (that can be used for timber extraction and production purposes) is eucalyptus (Zaiton et al., 2018). This can take just ten years to fully mature depending on the soil and climatic conditions where it is planted. As a result, there are many eucalyptus plantations in operation around the world, which account for c.1.5% of the total global forestry area (Binkley et al., 2017). Such plantations exist due to the inability of old-growth forests to fully meet the consumption needs of humans.

However, despite the implementation of domestic laws and regulations that are designed to protect old-growth forests, legal and illegal logging still exists due to its profitability (Dauvergne and Lister, 2011). This is often made easier due to the weak legal regimes and corrupt governments that exist in many parts of the world where old-growth forests reside, such as in the rainforests of the Amazon, Congo, and Southeast Asia. Within these areas, deforestation is rife.

Whilst it is important to state that humans have always had a significant impact upon forests (due to their ability to provide shelter, firewood, and other such sustenance), the rate of deforestation has increased dramatically since the mid-20th century, mirroring the rise of industrial capitalism that is visible in contemporary Western societies. According to Williams (2003: 421), '555 million hectares of global forestry vanished' between 1950 and

2000, an area roughly 42 times the size of England. Similarly, Boekhout van Solinge and Kuijpers (2013: 199) denote that 'since the 1960s, almost 20 percent of the Amazon has been deforested.' But why is this important? If trees are renewable and can be replanted, does it matter if they are consumed from old-growth forests or new plantations?

The short answer is yes. From an ecological point of view, old-growth forests are tremendously important, as they are rich in biodiversity. The forests of the Congo basin (which constitute around 20% of the earth's remaining tropical moist forests), for example, contain '70% of the total plants cover' in the entirety of Africa, and 36% of over 1000 bird species that habitat in the Congo forests are native and endemic (Bele et al., 2014: 2). This means that if deforestation continues in the Congo, widespread species loss will ensue as the habitat that supports such an abundance of life is either abolished or fragmented. Therefore, whilst new plantations do still provide a habitat, they are significantly less rich in biodiversity. Furthermore, old-growth forests are quintessential carbon stores, sequestering carbon dioxide in return for oxygen (Raihan et al., 2019). Approximately 12% to 15% of global carbon dioxide emissions are attributed to the deforestation of old-growth forests (Van der Werf et al., 2009: 738). This is because when an old-growth tree is felled, it releases the carbon it has been storing for hundreds of years into the atmosphere.

The reasons for deforestation are many and complex but are almost always the result of human interference. For example, of the deforestation in the Brazilian Amazon, Boekhout van Solinge and Kuijpers (2013: 199) attribute more than 70% to land conversion for cattle farming and soy cultivation. Of this deforestation, 60% to 90% is illegal according to varying estimates, and while deforestation has slowed in the wake of recent environmental activism and media attention, the 'Amazon rainforest still disappears with an average speed of more than one football pitch per minute' (Boekhout van Solinge, 2016: 374).

1.2.2 The extinction of the earth's ecology and non-human species

Whilst deforestation is one example of how species may become extinct as a direct consequence of human actions, there are several other reasons. These include (but are not limited to) climate change, poaching (for ivory or as a form of competition), pollution, urban development, and food consumption. In fact, rapid species extinction of the 21st century is of such concern to scientists that it has been described as the sixth mass extinction episode in the earth's history (Ceballos et al., 2017).

However, whilst the cessation of several species of non-human animals is often envisaged as part of the current mass extinction, it also applies to plants, vegetation, and other ecologies that support fauna and humans alike. For example, Pimm and Raven (2017) suggest that 20% to 33% of known global plant species are currently at risk of extinction. The significance of the risk of extinction (and a general reduction in the availability) of plant life is of vital importance to the earth's ability to feed and sustain non-human animals and, as such, is a vital part of the food chain. As Johnson et al. (2017: 270) reveal, 'all species are connected to others through ecological interactions. Extinctions therefore reverberate through ecosystems, as do extirpations of local populations and declines in abundance, which are widespread even in species not close to extinction.' As a result it is clear that species extinction of all kinds is detrimental to the earth's ability to support life.

Another seminal example of biodiversity and species decline can be witnessed in the oceans of planet Earth. Species degeneration in such water systems again has many contributing factors including pollution; over-fishing or over-exploitation of sea animals; habitat destruction and fragmentation (either through climate change or direct human activity); and poaching (such as Japanese whale hunting or the notorious Faroese Grindadráp pilot whale poaching tradition). As a result of such human interference, the biodiversity of the oceans is changing and becoming less organised. As Worm et al. (2006: 787) acknowledge:

> Changes in marine biodiversity are directly caused by exploitation, pollution, and habitat destruction, or indirectly through climate change and related perturbations of ocean biogeochemistry. Although marine extinctions are only slowly uncovered at the global scale, regional ecosystems such as estuaries, coral reefs, and coastal and oceanic fish communities are rapidly losing populations, species, or entire functional groups.

However, whilst many factors contribute to biodiversity loss in the oceans, pollution is one major factor that is a direct consequence of human activity, symbolising anthropocentric dominance of the natural world.

1.2.3. The pollution of water systems with plastics and non-biodegradable matter

The oceans are becoming more and more polluted with plastics and other non-biodegradable matter due to the increase in consumption of plastics globally. Western nations in particular have been criticised for their contribution to this problem due to the disposable, 'throw-away' culture that dominates modern consumption habits (Dauvergne and Lister, 2011).

Unfortunately, plastic has some key properties that make its management as a waste challenging. As Wabnitz and Nichols (2010: 1) suggest, (many) plastics are 'inexpensive, lightweight, strong, durable, (and) corrosion resistant.' This means that they are excellent sources of packaging and are also used in the making of many consumer goods (such as toothbrushes and electrical products). However, plastics are difficult to recycle, meaning much waste ends up in landfill, in incineration, or dumped at sea.

According to Lebreton et al. (2018: 1) 'around 60% of the plastic produced is less dense than seawater.' This means that – when in the ocean – 40% of the plastic will sink towards the seabed, and 60% is subject to ocean currents and other elements that may cause it to move (such as wind and sea animals). Subsequently some plastics become washed up on coastlines, some eventually lose their buoyancy and do sink, and others become trapped in currents termed gyres (Lebreton et al., 2018). The largest known gyre lies in the Pacific Ocean and has been dubbed colloquially the Great Pacific Garbage Patch (GPGP), roughly twice the size of the US state of Texas (Huang, 2017: 101). The GPGP is problematic because it can enter the food chain as a result of being consumed by aquatic animals. According to Wabnitz and Nichols (2010: 1):

> The bodies of almost all marine species, ranging in size from plankton to marine mammals, and including some of the wildest and most vulnerable species on the planet – animals that make nearly their entire living far from humans – now contain plastic. Sixty percent of 6,136 surface plankton net tows conducted in the western North Atlantic Ocean and Caribbean Sea from 1986 to 2008 contained buoyant plastic pieces, typically millimetres in size. . . . Plastics turn up in bird nests, are worn by hermit crabs instead of shells, and are present in sea turtle, whale and albatross stomachs. . . . Over 260 species, including invertebrates, turtles, fish, seabirds and mammals, have been reported to ingest or become entangled in plastic debris, resulting in impaired movement and feeding, reduced reproductive output, lacerations, ulcers, and death.

This state of affairs clearly presents an environmental injustice that is the direct result of the human production and consumption of plastics. The GPGP demonstrates the failure of human societies and legal systems to adequately manage plastic waste. But why has the law largely failed to protect marine environments?

The problem stems from power. From the 15th to the 20th centuries, powerful European nations such as the United Kingdom (UK), Belgium, France, and Spain (amongst many others) made multiple attempts to expand their empires through a long and violent process of colonisation. This led to all habitable land on earth becoming the possession of monarchs. Subsequently, legal systems arose in these kingdoms, often as a check and balance on the absolute authority of the monarchy. However, the sheer uninhabitability of the world's oceans meant that, at the time of mass colonisation, the seas were used merely as a form of transportation (and sustenance) rather than a territory to be occupied, overthrown, and defeated. As a result, laws governing the oceans (particularly outside of immediate coastal regions) remained practically non-existent until the 1972 Stockholm Conference, which was the first legally binding international legal agreement between nations regarding the governance of the oceans (Harrison, 2017: 5).

Due to ocean environments being largely uninhabitable, they have escaped the authority of domestic law, and most of the earth's ocean environments are *governed* (in the loosest sense of the word) through international laws inclusive of custom, treaties, and general principles (Harrison, 2017: 7). There are, however, two problems with utilising international law for oceanic protection. Firstly, such laws are very difficult, if not impossible, to enforce. As a result, much crime that occurs on the high seas (such as the dumping of wastes) goes unnoticed, creating an incredible dark figure of environmental crime. Secondly, the necessity to strictly abide by international legal agreements is weaker than domestic law because of the lack of both enforcement and accountability for illegal actions. This problem is manifested in the 'free will' nature of international law, as adequately described by Harrison (2017: 7):

> At its simplest, international law can be understood as a normative framework that governs relations between States or between States and other actors with international legal personality. Given the lack of hierarchy between States, international law is by and large a decentralized system, based upon consent to relevant norms. In other words, the rules of law binding upon States . . . emanate from their own free will.

This state of affairs has resulted in oceanic management, protection, and cleanup falling into the hands of non-governmental organisations who recognise the failings of international law and the necessity to do something about marine pollution in the interests of both human and oceanic life. The Ocean Cleanup (2020; see also: Cressey, 2016) for example, is dedicated to developing technological solutions to ocean plastics, demonstrating the positive side of the human conscience. However, whilst such work is undeniably beneficial for marine environments and a step in the right direction, questions remain around what is done with the plastic that is collected from the oceans. The best and most positive solution has been to model consumer products out of the plastic (although this does not guarantee the plastic will not re-enter the ocean as pollution at a later date). Other options include standard practices for dealing with plastics such as incineration or dumping in landfill. Furthermore, Ocean Cleanup operations can be seen as a reactive solution to environmental harms which fail to address the causes of plastic pollution in the first instance. Additionally, such Ocean Cleanup projects only assess visible pollution of plastic at the ocean surface and largely fail to address largescale problems of non-buoyant plastics that adversely impact sub-surface marine life.

Due to the shortcomings of reactive Ocean Cleanup operations, a legal approach to preventing plastic pollution in the first instance remains a credible option. However, as has been previously noted, current international frameworks are quite visibly failing to prevent environmental harm, and gyres continue to collect masses of plastics. As Bigagli (2016: 155) points out, 'several voices in the literature point to the fact that this legal framework is fragmented, inadequate to tackle the challenges of managing the oceans, and in need of a paradigm shift.' The central premise of this book is that such a paradigm shift could be achieved by utilising the principles of earth jurisprudence and that green criminology can help to provide a conceptual framework that considers environmental harms as well as crimes.

Unfortunately, it is not just plastics that pollute the earth's oceans. There are several other human endeavours that impact marine life, such as over-fishing, accidental pollution (such as oil spills or dropped trawler netting), and various forms of dumping of hazardous wastes. A classic example of the latter comes in the guise of cruise ships that dump their waste in international waters, where the jurisdiction and rule of law is weak. Cruise ship waste pollution can come in several different forms but can generally be categorised into organic waste (such as foods) and inorganic wastes (hazardous substances such as paint, medical waste, and cleaning agents; Carić and Mackelworth, 2014). There are generally three options for dealing with this waste. The first is to use disposal options at ports (which vary considerably in their abilities and capacity around the world). Secondly, wastes can be incinerated either onshore or onboard cruise ships (for those that have installed such technology). The third – and, perhaps significantly, the cheapest option – is to dump the waste at sea. Estimations as to the volume of wastes generated from cruise ships varies and is likely to increase as the global cruise tourism industry itself expands. However, the United States Environmental Protection Agency (2008, in: Carić and Mackelworth, 2014: 352) estimates up to 3.5 kg of waste per person per day are generated from cruise ships. From a legal perspective, the global lack of oceanic environmental protection leads to cruise ships releasing their wastes into the sea untreated. As Carić and Mackelworth (2014: 352) convey when discussing cruise-line waste pollution in the Adriatic Sea:

> While organic waste can only be legally disposed of beyond 12 NM (nautical miles) from the Mediterranean coast, there is no effective manner of controlling waste disposal practices on board ships. Various types of waste are dumped at sea creating problems such as

eutrophication, hypoxia and bio-accumulation of toxins. . . . (Furthermore), the problem of storage of waste on-board cruisers is a significant issue, especially as space is at a premium.

Section 1.2.3. tackled significant issues around waste pollution at sea, specifically focusing on cruise tourism and the accumulation of plastics in gyres. Furthermore, there has been a discussion of the environmental consequences of the weak domestic and international laws that currently 'govern' the oceans. The next section (1.2.4.) will move on to discussing the consumption of sentient animals for the fulfilment of Western dietary habits, providing a further (and final, for this chapter), example of the domination of humans over the natural world and the current failure of legal systems to prevent environmental harms.

1.2.4. The use, abuse, and consumption of animals to satisfy Western diets

Section 1.2.1. has already highlighted that the demand for meat is having a detrimental impact on the environment, whereby one of the key drivers of deforestation in the Amazon rainforest is to simply create land suitable for rearing cattle (Boekhout van Solinge and Kuijpers, 2013). In fact, Brazil is now one of the largest exporters of beef in the world, which contributes approximately 7% of the country's gross domestic product (GDP; Schierhorn et al., 2016: 87). However, whilst deforestation is an incredibly important issue pertaining to meat production, it is not the only environmental harm that results from the production of animals for human consumption. Exported animals must be transported from the source of origin to the requisite market to be purchased, which incurs further greenhouse gas emissions associated with transport powered by fossil fuels. It is undeniable that the global demand for beef, pork, poultry, fish, and other consumable animal fleshes creates greenhouse gas emissions (through deforestation and transportation), emissions that simply would not exist if the demand was not present. Therefore, the production of non-human animal products can be seen as a consequence of market forces that are underpinned by capitalism.

The seminal characteristics of the capitalist system are profit maximisation, the private ownership of the means of production, and the emergence of social and ecological inequality based on the unequal distribution of power and capital (Sebastian, 2017: 167). This state of affairs has resulted in huge numbers of animals being reared for the sole purposes of satisfying meat consumption demands. Whilst it is impossible to accurately account for all these animals, Rowe (2011: 3) estimates the death toll to be more than 30 billion per year worldwide, highlighting the extent of animal consumption.

However, it is not just the climatic implications of mass animal production that is concerning from an environmental point of view. It is widely recognised that the animals consumed in Western diets (beef, poultry, pork, etc.) are sentient beings – that is, they have the capacity to feel pleasure and pain (Matheny, 2006). Therefore, the extent to which sentient animals should be protected from practices that incur a considerable level of pain (as humans – one form of sentient beings – also wish to be protected) is open to debate. What is apparent, though, is that human legal systems are currently designed to facilitate meat production in spite of the environmental consequences and species injustices.

A final consideration with regards to meat consumption surrounds the everyday practices associated with production processes. Up until the 1970s, 90% of food was consumed in the country of origin (Parker and Johnson, 2019: 207). Today, global demand for meat products has led to increasing exportation of meat and the transformation of meat production from small-scale farms producing low-quantities of meat to large-scale farms and slaughterhouses where thousands of animals can be cultivated in one place. This has led to the emergence of cruel and inhumane practices where the profits of mass production are prioritised over animal welfare, a situation that human legal systems have failed to adequately address. As Rowe (2011: 12–13) explains:

> Industrial agriculture supplants the free range, grass fed practices of subsistence based farms with Concentrated Animal Feeding Operations . . . where thousands – in the case of egg-laying hens, hundreds of thousands and millions – of livestock (i.e., living inventory) are reared in one facility. (Subsequently, there are many deprivations) of basic comforts; rearing animals in crowded confinement stalls and pens; veil crates, gestation crates, and battery cages; tail docking and beak clipping; hormones and anti-biotics; broken limbs and dysfunctional organs . . . and a disassembly line that never stops mutilating and killing – these are the standard practices of industrial meat production.

This quotation clearly demonstrates the inhumane methods of producing meat. From an environmental perspective, a secondary harm pertains to the transportation of meat from the place of rearing to the location of consumption. Human-made laws facilitate this state of affairs and have clearly failed to prevent pervasive environmental harm.

1.3. The structure of this book

This initial chapter has introduced a variety of case studies that have sought to exemplify the current magnitude of environmental harms and crimes, considering them on a global scale. Additionally, there has been constant discussion of the failure and, in fact, active facilitation of such harms from governments and human legal systems. The examples of deforestation, biodiversity loss, ocean plastics, and meat consumption were employed to explore these themes in more detail.

The purpose of starting with a chapter that described some of the ongoing cataclysmic anthropocentrically induced environmental harms was to provide a solid foundation from which to begin debates around the solutions to such environmental problems. These will be discussed in detail throughout the remainder of this book.

The next chapter will move on from specifically identifying real-life cases of environmental harm to discussing the historical and theoretical foundations of a green criminology. The seminal aim of this book is to encourage cross-collaboration between green criminology and earth jurisprudence, two disciplines that actively seek to identify and provide solutions to environmental harms and crimes. Therefore, considering what green criminology *is* (and what it is not) is a logical starting point for discussing some of the academic literature concerned with the types of environmental issues identified in this opening chapter. Proceeding green criminology will be a similar exploration into the historical and theoretical foundations of wild law and earth jurisprudence in Chapter 3.

Chapter 4 ('Uniting green criminology and earth jurisprudence') will bring together the two disciplines discussing their similarities and shared goals (identifying and theorising the reasons behind environmental harms and crimes). Doing so will highlight the advantages inherent in uniting scholars operating within both disciplines, which will enable communication, information-sharing, collaboration on research projects, and provide important solutions to the environmental, ecological, and species injustices that currently plague planet Earth. Part of this will include the benefit of green criminologists engaging with the philosophy of earth jurisprudence as a preventative, holistic solution to environmental harms, something that is currently only provided in detail by treadmill of production (ToP) theory (Stretesky et al., 2014).

Whilst it is recognised that the implementation of an earth jurisprudence into human law is incredibly challenging considering quintessential state–corporate relationships that together facilitate environmental harm, Chapter 5 ('Earth jurisprudence in practice: success stories') will identify a number of constitutional and legal success stories whereby principles of earth jurisprudence have been efficaciously enshrined into human legal systems. Doing so will ultimately emphasise the potential of earth jurisprudence in addressing environmental harm whilst simultaneously providing green criminology with a preventative solution to environmental harms (something which, as a discipline, it is argued, is currently lacking).

2 Historical and theoretical foundations of a 'green' criminology

2.1. Introduction

Chapter 1 drew upon academic and scientific literature to exemplify the magnitude of environmental and ecological harm and degradation that is occurring now – on a global scale – and is the direct result of human actions. The opening chapter also highlighted the contemporary nature of the situation, noting that such intense environmental degradation is a relatively recent phenomenon that has intensified since the turn of the 21st century. Several disciplines have contributed to research on these climatic changes in recent decades. One such discipline is green criminology. The aim of Chapter 2 is to introduce the reader to the historical and theoretical foundations of a 'green' criminology in an attempt to increase understanding of the seminal arguments and philosophies contained within. Furthermore, doing this will enable stipulation over where green criminology is situated within broader debates surrounding global climate change.

Finally, discussing historical and theoretical foundations enables us to understand the limitations of the study of green criminology. One such limitation is the lack of an overarching solution to the global problem of widespread environmental and ecological harm. Whilst many green criminologists have done incredible work in exposing environmental harms such as the illegal trade of flora and fauna across borders (Maher and Wyatt, 2017; Wyatt, 2009), most scholars offer only secular, tailored solutions to such problems (such as more stringent laws to deter illegal deforestation, for example). Viewing the work of green criminology in this way identifies the lack of contributions made to broader, more holistic solutions to global environmental harms. Although some scholars have identified the structural problems and inequalities that lead to environmental harm, rooting their arguments in theories of political economy (Stretesky et al., 2014), few have attempted to offer a more generic, holistic solution.

It is recognised within this chapter that such a 'one-size-fits-all' approach conjures its own problems (whether it is realistic – or even naïve – to assume that one approach or law, theory, or idea, could prevent all environmental harm). However there is some evidence to suggest that more all-encompassing approaches are being developed, such as Higgins et al.'s (2013) proposal for a law on ecocide.

This chapter will consider all of these issues. Chapter 3 will move away from green criminology and on to introducing and evaluating the historical and theoretical foundations of an earth jurisprudence. Chapters 4 and 5 will identify why earth jurisprudence can act as a holistic solution to environmental harms, thereby providing a useful solution to the multitude of problems identified by green criminologists. It is hoped that such an analysis will spark future debate and collaboration between green criminologists and those scholars discussing the importance of earth jurisprudence and wild law.

2.2. What is green criminology?

An exploration into the historical and theoretical foundations of green criminology must begin with a detailed explanation of what green criminology *is*. Doing so enables the establishment of a basic platform from which to assess and critically analyse key arguments within green criminology. Furthermore, starting with the basics of what green criminology is (and, importantly, *what it is not*) enables answers to be given to some basic preliminary questions that a person new to the subject may ask in order to gain an initial understanding of the topic. Questions such as: What are the overarching aims and objectives of green criminology and green criminologists? What does green criminology seek to achieve? What types of crimes does a green criminology consider? Who are the key scholars writing and researching within green criminology? And what exactly is it that they are trying to understand, measure, and theorise?

To begin to answer such questions, it is important to note that green criminology has been described as a loose *perspective* as opposed to a unitary, rigid theory (South, 1998; South et al., 2013: White, 2008a: 14). This means that scholars often choose to situate their research within the green criminology perspective, as it can serve as a useful tool for explaining the importance and significance of their research into various environmental harms and environmental crimes. However, whilst such a green criminological umbrella (Lampkin, 2016) is undoubtedly useful as a means to situate one's research, it must be noted at this early stage that there are several different theoretical concepts and approaches that are encompassed under the umbrella of green criminology (Lynch and Stretesky, 2014: 77). These include political economic, green-critical, green-cultural, eco-feminist, and environmental victimological typologies (although this is by no means an exhaustive list). Such approaches will be discussed in greater detail in Sections 2.4. ('Problems with the term "green" and the positioning of green criminology') and 2.5. ('Limitations of green criminology').

Green criminology has often been described as a perspective because of the diversity of research that has been conducted under the umbrella of green criminology. In essence, any research that discusses environmental, ecological, or species abuse, degradation, harm, or crime can be encompassed within green criminological literature. This means that green criminology is extremely diverse, multi-disciplinary, and its net is cast far and wide. Such diversity has often been described as one of the strengths of green criminology (Cao and Wyatt, 2016). As South et al. (2013: 28, emphasis in original) denote:

> Green criminology is not intended to be a unitary enterprise. Diversity is one of its great strengths and it is most helpfully seen as a capacious and evolving *perspective* . . . a loose framework or set of intellectual, empirical and political orientations toward problems (harms, offences and crimes related to the environment, different species and the planet). Importantly, it is also an 'open' perspective and framework, arising from within the tradition(s) of critical criminology; at the same time, it actively seeks inter- and multi-disciplinary engagement. It is both a network of interested individuals and a forum for sharing and debating ideas.

This quote typifies what green criminology *is*, an open framework, network or perspective from which to conduct research and debate ideas concerning environmental harms and crimes. It also demonstrates the difficulty in defining 'green criminology,' the very name of which is highly contested (see Section 2.4.).

'Green' criminology (quite visibly) has its roots within its parent discipline – *criminology*. However, green criminology has been interpreted as a particular radical (Lynch, 1990) and critical (Sollund, 2015; South and Brisman, 2012) strand of criminology that serves to overcome some of the perceived failings and limitations of the larger discipline of criminology. This idea manifests itself in the very foundations and roots of criminological discourse where there can be found a conflict regarding the basic nature of study. Should criminology, for example, focus solely on the study of *crimes* (violation of criminal laws)? Or should the focus be wider to include the study of *harms* (some of which are considered crimes, whilst many are not)?

These discussions are embedded within the notion of crime having *no ontological reality* (Hillyard et al., 2004; Hulsman, 1986: 64; Newburn,

2007). This means that the term 'crime' is a human construct developed to describe a particular form of human behaviour that is contrary to the national (and international) laws of the locality where the crime (or behaviour violation) was committed. If we use a standard definition of 'crime' or 'criminology,' we can instantly see the limitations. For example, Wolfgang (1963: 155, emphasis in original) defines criminology as a 'body of *scientific* knowledge about crime.' Similarly, Cressey (1951: 551) suggests that it is necessary to 'restrict the use of the word "crime" to behaviour which is so defined by the criminal law.' These two quotes insinuate that there is an historical and innate need to define crime and criminology in such a way that aligns the subject with the objective, positivistic scientific method. Therefore, criminology has historically been a discipline that seeks to measure, theorise, and understand *criminal* behaviours.

As a result, conventional definitions and understandings of criminology are deep rooted in the requirements of the discipline to be concerned with behaviours that violate criminal laws. To some degree, green criminology still respects this notion and continues to research, theorise, and offer solutions to orthodox criminological problems (the illegal trafficking of plants and animals, for instance). Fundamentally though, green crimes can also be said to have no ontological reality and similarly manifest themselves in the human imagination. As Lynch and Stretesky (2003: 218) suggest, 'green crimes, like other crimes, are social constructions influenced by social locations and power relations in society.'

However, several scholars (see: Hillyard et al., 2004) have composed highly influential work to suggest that criminology should be preoccupied with behaviours that create *harm as well as crime* (deviating from the conventional contours of criminology), with harm being considered the more relevant and suitable term that covers a range of *deviant* behaviours. This is in contradiction to a criminology that focuses solely on the violation of criminal laws that have no ontological reality. Such a modern take on the crime-versus-harm juxtaposition has resulted in a parallel criminological discipline – that of zemiology – which has been described very simply as the study of social harms (Hillyard and Tombs, 2017).

The significance of this crime/harm conundrum is very important in the understanding of green criminology because scholars using a green criminological perspective 'recognise that something ought to be done about harmful activities irrespective of their legality' (Lampkin, 2016: 31). For most green criminologists, *harm* is a more just object of study, regardless of whether that harm has been defined as a crime. The significance of the notion of harm arguably stems from an understanding of the *dark figure* of crime, which refers to 'all that criminal behaviour that we do not know about,' those crimes that are 'not recognised, not reported and not recorded' (Walklate, 2005: 36). Due to green criminology's broad area of study, the focus of several scholars is not necessarily on humans but is often concentrated on non-human species, ecological life, and the global climate. It is arguable that these 'participants' often escape inclusion within the criminal law merely because of their non-human status and, as a result, transition into the dark figure of environmental crime. When discussing the phenomenology of environmental criminal offences, Batrićević (2018: 139) suggests that the dark figures of crime are one of the eight most common characteristics of environmental crime (alongside other such commonalities as the often transnational and organised nature of green crimes).

In fact, many practices that are environmentally damaging conversely have a negative impact for humans (such as air pollution) and are often legal despite their harmful consequences. That said, it is clear that there is not just a dark figure of environmental *crime* but also a much larger *dark figure of environmental harm*. As White (2013a: 26) suggests, 'of concern to green criminologists is how best to measure the dark figure of environmental crime – those harms presently unreported or undocumented or unacknowledged as environmental crimes.'

Section 2.2. has discussed some of the basic theoretical underpinnings of green criminology including the consideration of the subject as a *perspective* rather than a theory; the radical and critical 'fit' of green criminology within the larger criminological discourse; as well as a discussion around the crime/harm nexus. The next Section (2.3.) will move on to discuss the development and early life of green criminology, which serves to place the study in context before discussing the inherent problems with the term '*green* criminology' in Section 2.4.

2.3. The emergence of a 'green' criminology

Several authors have attributed the coining of the term 'green' criminology to the seminal work of Michael Lynch in 1990 (see: Goyes and South, 2017; Heydon, 2019: 7; Johnson, 2017: 91; Spencer and Fitzgerald, 2013: 211). However, it is important to clarify that criminological thought on green issues significantly pre-dates Lynch's call for a specifically green form of criminology (Goyes and South, 2017; White, 2013b: 17). Therefore, whilst it could be interpreted that green criminological research has increased exponentially since Lynch's (1990) initial call (perhaps due to the more common and severe forms of global environmental harms – see Chapter 1), it does not devalue any previous work conducted in the area of environmental crime. Goyes and South (2017: 165), for instance, suggest that pre-1990 scholarship 'has been forgotten' but 'deserves acknowledgement' given the inclusionary nature of the green criminological perspective.

However, it is worth considering why Lynch (1990) coined the term 'green criminology.' Was the timing merely a matter of chance, or is 1990 of some importance? Why was the colour 'green' employed to precede the term 'criminology' (as opposed to other words or colours)? And what were the significant factors that led Lynch (1990) to call for a new area within the parent discipline of criminology?

Matthew Hall (2013: 5–6), amongst others, has shed some important light in this area. He suggests that the emergence of green criminology, for Lynch (1990), was the coming together of at least three movements: ecofeminism, environmental racism, and ecological socialisms (terms that all pre-date 'green criminology'). Such movements argued that the 'effects of environmental degradation fall disproportionately on women compared to men' (ecofeminism), disproportionately on some races (environmental racism), and finally, that the socially excluded 'bear the brunt' of environmental degradation due to the inherent inequalities between 'wealth and power in society' (Hall, 2013: 5, see also: Collin, 1994; Griffin, 1978; and Pepper, 1993).

Therefore, it is important to understand that the roots of green criminology manifest themselves not just in environmental harms and crimes but deeper into certain 'green' sociological projects. This helps to explain the diversity of green criminological literature, which not only identifies specific forms of environmental degradation (such as air pollution, oil spills, and precious metals extraction) but also often provides a sociological account for the reasons behind environmental harm. For example, there is still a considerable body of (recent) green criminological scholarship that considers ecofeminism (Beirne, 2019; Sollund, 2013), environmental racism (Stretesky and Lynch, 1998; Stretesky and McKie, 2016), and ecological socialisms (Brisman and South, 2016; Gaarder, 2013).

Despite Lynch's (1990) call for a 'green' criminology, it was not until the turn of the millennium that academic research began making specific reference to its situation within the 'new' field of green criminology. South's (1998) call for a green perspective was one of the first specific developments of theoretical green criminology, built upon by Lynch and Stretesky (2003), who considered in detail the 'meaning of green' criminology, concluding that solutions to green crimes were manifested in major economic and political reorganisation (see: Heydon, 2019: 7), giving the term 'green' a political connotation. However, despite these seminal advancements in green criminology, several scholars have alluded to the problems inherent with adopting the term 'green,' offering various other adjacent titles that they believe better encapsulate what green criminology *is*.

2.4. Problems with the term 'green' and the positioning of green criminology

Debate of the term 'green' as a satisfactory (or unsatisfactory) heading to describe criminologists' preoccupation with environmental harms and crimes really began with Lynch and Stretesky's (2003) seminal article evaluating the meaning of the term 'green.' This article was one of the first to attempt to define green criminology and can be said to have set the course for future discussions on the value, meaning, and definition of green criminology. Within their article, Lynch and Stretesky (2003) provided two distinct views on the term 'green.' The first was an *environmental justice* perspective whereby green crimes are characterised as acts that 'may or may not violate existing rules and regulations' (Lynch and Stretesky, 2003: 227). The second – a *corporate perspective* – perceived green crimes as 'unauthorised acts or omissions that violate the law and are therefore subject to criminal prosecution and sanctions' (Situ and Emmons, 2000: 3, in: Lynch and Stretesky, 2003: 229). As a result, it is easy to see that considerations of both crime (corporatist perspective) and harm (environmental justice perspective) are fundamental to the understanding of green criminology (following on from Section 2.3.).

Mark Halsey (2004) immediately responded to Lynch and Stretesky's (2003) definitional debate by offering a robust critique of their work in his seminal article published in the *British Journal of Criminology* entitled 'Against "Green" Criminology.' For Halsey (2004), Lynch and Stretesky's (2003) rationale for embedding a 'green' approach within political arguments was flawed. Lynch and Stretesky (2003) argued that the environmental justice perspective was the most beneficial way to view green criminology considering the crime/harm nexus. However, their justification of this was (perhaps unsurprisingly) entrenched within Lynch's (1990) rationale for a 'green' criminology, which, as Section 2.3. demonstrated, evolved from ecofeminism, environmental racism, and eco-socialist movements. This led Lynch and Stretesky (2003) to align their green criminological arguments within not just broader debates on environmental justice but the political manifestations that naturally accompanied that perspective. As Lynch and Stretesky (2003: 231) suggest: 'We argue that being green implies more than holding values favouring environmental protection: it also entails a political stance wherein it is acknowledged that solutions to environmental degradation may require substantial economic and political reorganization.'

Halsey (2004: 835) agreed with Lynch and Stretesky (2003) insofar that the term 'green' carries with it unavoidable 'political baggage.' However, Halsey (2004: 835) perceived this inescapable alignment with politics as a failure to 'capture the inter-subjective, inter-generational, (and) . . . inter-ecosystemic processes which combine to produce scenarios of harm.' One of the central concerns for Halsey (2004) regarding the political connotations of the word 'green' was the alignment with market forces. The problem here was that market forces imply an element of control over the solutions to green crimes, the answers for which are to 'modify (but not radically alter)' environmental laws, industrial processes, and environmental enforcement (Halsey, 2004: 836). Correspondingly, Halsey (2004: 836) drew a definitive line between those people who are 'inside' or 'outside' the realms of environmental criminal liability, implying that some powerful entities (i.e. large corporations and lawmakers) may be 'untouchable.' Therefore, the inter-relationship between power, lawmaking, politics, and ecosystemic harm – for Halsey (2004: 835) – requires the label of 'green' to be 'jettisoned from criminological discourse.'

However, to some extent, what Halsey (2004) and Lynch and Stretesky (2003) do attach importance to is the notion of *harm* within the meaning and definition of green criminology. As Halsey (2004: 849, emphasis in original) suggests, 'the problem is not crime, but the limits placed upon who and what can count as criminal subjects and/or criminal objects. More than this, *the problem is how to think beyond crime as a useful category of thought.*' These early debates into the nature and meaning of green criminology have cemented the critical alignment of green criminology within the broader subject of criminology. As a result, the notion of harm alongside crime still resonates in recent definitions of green criminology. For example, White (2019: 248) defines green criminology as broadly referring to 'the study by criminologists of environmental harms (that may incorporate wider definitions of crime than that provided in strictly legal definitions).'

Furthermore (regarding the politics of the term 'green'), Potter (2013: 125) argues that green symbolises a partisan ideological approach to the study of environmental harm whereby 'it is inferred that green criminologists are on the side of nature.' Discussing the subjective reasoning behind one's engagement with academic research generally (and therefore applied to the study of environmental harm) would necessitate evaluation of the ontological, epistemological, and axiological nature of research, which is beyond the scope of this book. However, it must be noted that Potter (2013: 125) raises an important point in suggesting that the term 'green' leaves 'green criminology open to criticism for being overly ideological and overtly political, and therefore particularly prone to accusations of bias.'

Finally (regarding the political insinuations of the term 'green'), whilst one of the strengths of green criminology is its diversity and inter-disciplinary acceptance, Ruggiero and South (2013: 363) denote that 'some (scholars) may feel that their scientific neutrality and credibility will be questioned if they are associated with an explicitly "green" position, group or body of work.' Whilst many scholars may embrace such a stance, it does not detract from the fact that some may be put off from addressing environmental harms and crimes (or at least situating their research within the green criminological perspective) purely due to the term 'green' and any ensuing political ramifications.

However, the political connotation of the word 'green' is not the only argument for (as Halsey would put it) *jettisoning* the term from criminological discourse. Another problem stems from green criminology's 'branding issues' if (as it seems increasingly likely) green criminology remains the commonly appropriated lexicon. As Brisman (2015) rightly suggests, the term 'green' means different things to different people and can vary across cultures and contexts. When applied to branding issues, Halsey (2013: 107) suggests that the term 'green' has been adopted by corporations (singling out BP, Halliburton, Dow Chemical, and BHP Billiton specifically) as a marketing strategy to represent their business as 'being green' despite their undeniable negative contributions to ecological destruction and climate change (a classic example being the notorious *Deepwater Horizon* oil spill in April 2010). Despite this branding argument, Ruggiero and South (2013: 363) suggest that the underpinning quintessential values and essence of green criminology and its recognition of being a *perspective* as opposed to a cemented theory imply that 'green criminology need not be employed by those who do not find it useful.' After all, green criminology has been adequately described as a platform for research, knowledge and debate on issues pertaining to environmental harm (South et al., 2013: 28) rather than a regimented criminological theory.

So far, this section has highlighted some of the pertinent strengths and weakness of the term 'green criminology.' It is widely accepted that the term '*environmental* criminology' would more accurately reflect the aims and values of a criminology sub-type that focuses on human interactions with the natural world that generate harms or crimes. However, as many have previously noted (Hall, 2013: 4; South, 2014: 8; White, 2008a: 6–7), the term 'environmental criminology' has been ascribed (perhaps prematurely) as a field pre-occupied with place-based criminology, situational crime approaches, and analysis rooted in combating criminal behaviour that takes place repeatedly in particular, and often urban, localities (such as drug dealing or various forms of anti-social behaviours). It could be argued, then, that this is one of the primary reasons green criminology has failed to shake off the colour green (i.e. the term 'environmental criminology' has been taken, and there is no alternative phrase that better encompasses the study of environmental harm and crime than the now well-established term 'green criminology').

On the contrary, several authors have made attempts to offer different lexical choices as either replacements or advances to the term 'green criminology' (Brisman and South, 2020a: 4–5). Some examples include '*conservation* criminology' (Gibbs et al., 2010; Gore, 2017; Halsey, 2013); '*eco-global* criminology' (White, 2010); '*climate change* criminology' (White, 2018), and '*eco-crime*' (Walters, 2010), to name a few. Furthermore, there are several mini-disciplinary offshoots of green criminology under a selection of other related titles such as '*atmospheric justice*' (Walters, 2013), '*species justice*' (Nurse, 2013), and even '*astro-green criminology*' (Lampkin, 2020b; Takemura, 2019) – the consideration of environmental harms (mainly pollutions) outside of planet Earth. Each of these offshoots represents a specific area of focus on issues of environmental harm, but they are still conceptualised and encapsulated under the broad umbrella of green criminology.

The different terminologies that have arisen in the last decade or so have arguably attempted to address green criminology's branding issue (Halsey, 2013) and the problems associated with the term 'green.' However, it could be argued that if we are to accept that green criminology is more of a *perspective* as opposed to a theory (South, 1998; South et al., 2013) then the lexicon 'green' can still be seen to serve a useful purpose. In fact, several green criminologists have embraced the term 'green' and offered a range of additional colours (Brisman, 2015; Lynch and Stretesky, 2003; White, 2008a) to help contextualise what green criminology is – a diverse rainbow of colours which represents the breadth of study. To make this easier to understand, Table 2.1 provides a visual exploration of several different colours that can be explored within green criminology.

The benefit of thinking about green criminology in a multi-coloured fashion is that it enables the visualisation of where ones research sits upon the green criminology spectrum, depending on the focus of study (which may be purely ecological or may involve elements of interaction between humans and the environment). Furthermore, providing a spectrum of colours goes some way to addressing the limitations associated with a purely 'green' criminology (and the ensuing political machinations).

However, the difficultly with sub-dividing areas of research into coloured categories is that it is not always clear under which colour a particular study should operate. White (2005), for example, classified air pollution under 'brown' issues, with only a brief description of what brown issues entail (urban life and pollution). It could be argued that air pollution is a white, grey, or transparent issue depending on how you are subjectively perceiving air pollution (i.e. visualising car exhaust fumes, flaring of waste gases at fracking sites, or ozone depletion caused by air pollution – all of which could represent different colours). Similarly, oil spills was also considered a

Table 2.1 The Spectrum of Green Criminological Research

Colour	*Description*	*Adapted from*
Green criminology	The study of environmental harms and crimes	Lynch (1990)
Green issues for green criminology	Habitat destruction Wildlife loss Deforestation	White (2005: 278, 2008a: 98–99) See also: Brisman (2015: 179)
Brown issues for green criminology	Air pollution Oil spills Disposal of hazardous wastes	White (2005: 278, 2008a: 98–99) See also: Brisman (2015: 179)
White issues for green criminology	Genetically modified organisms Environmentally related communicable diseases	White (2005: 278, 2008a: 98–99) See also: Brisman (2015: 179)
Red-green issues for green criminology	Relate to the workplace Structural economic oppression Exploitation of the working class Polluting technologies in the workplace	Lynch and Stretesky (2003: 224–225)
Blue-green issues for green criminology	For Fussey and South (2012), blue represents 'security' (i.e. policing, law enforcement)	Brisman (2015: 179) Fussey and South (2012)
Grey-green issues for green criminology	Brisman (2015: 179) uses McClanahan's (2014) work on the criminalisation of household wastewater, known colloquially as 'greywater'	Brisman (2015: 179) McClanahan (2014)
Achromatopsic issues for green criminology	Climate change has been described as achromatopsic (colour-blind), as it affects everybody. However, it is still encompassed under green criminology because of the negative environmental effects of climate change and even as a red-green issue due to the uneven distribution of the effects on different groups (ethnicity, gender, class, income, religion etc.).	Brisman (2015: 180)

brown issue by White (2005) despite the very common black visualisation of spilled crude oils. Finally, whilst blue may represent security (i.e. policing), it is also clearly synonymous with water, rivers, streams, oceans, and the like (which has little to do with security).

Despite the drawbacks of distinguishing between different colours, the central premise of allowing green criminological research to feature anywhere on the spectrum enables one to clearly visualise the diversity of 'green' issues and the advantageous position of considering green criminology as a perspective. The next section will go on to critique green criminology in order to expose some of the gaps and fundamental flaws of the discipline. Doing so will pave the way for the remaining chapters of this book to identify how earth jurisprudence can go some way to filling some of those gaps.

2.5. Limitations of green criminology

As was stated in the previous section, Halsey (2013) identified a 'branding' issue with the term 'green,' which for him was too closely aligned with the green marketing strategies of large corporations who use the term to paint a sustainable picture whilst at the same time actively engaging in environmentally harmful industrial processes. This is certainly one of the indirect limitations of green criminology.

Furthermore, the political connotations of the word 'green' have been discussed (Halsey, 2004; Potter, 2013), including the thought that this may be off-putting for newcomers contemplating situating their research within green criminological debates (Ruggiero and South, 2013). Additionally on this point, Potter (2013: 125) goes as far as insinuating that 'concerns over the value positions inherent within green criminology have contributed to its remaining a niche specialism, kept apart from (and sometimes shunned by) the criminological mainstream.'

In terms of further criticism of green criminology, Potter (2013: 131–132) gives four overlapping arguments that are debated in Table 2.2.

The limitations of green criminology highlighted in this book so far can generally be considered open to debate and interpretation. For example, the extent to which focussing on the types of environmental degradation that are not specifically labelled as criminal (such as fishing or transportation powered by fossil fuels, for example) – as being worthy of inclusion in mainstream criminology is subject to debate. Many green criminologists believe that the study of environmental harm does have a place within criminology – as many *legal* behaviours are still environmentally degrading. Conversely, others have stated that harm is not the true remit of criminology (Potter, 2013) that seeks to address and explain purely *criminal* behaviours.

Table 2.2 Debates Surrounding the Limitations of Green Criminology

Argument	*Debate*	
	Critique of green criminology	*Problem with critique*
1	Those crimes that are not covered by the criminal law are 'simply beyond the remit of criminology' (Potter, 2013: 131).	The criminal law varies across time and space and, therefore, a criminology that only considers law violations risks failing to address the dark figure of crime (and even more so the dark of figure of harm). This is particularly relevant for green criminology, as many (if not most) environmental harm is produced through legal production processes.
2	'Where it is recognised that some of the subject area is indeed criminological . . . there is no need for a distinct green criminology as these crimes fall within the remit of established criminology' (Potter, 2013: 131).	Green criminology emerged in response to criminology's failings to address issues of both environmental harm and crime. As Halsey (2004: 834, emphasis in original) denotes: 'why at a time when most disciplines (e.g. politics, economics, history, cultural studies) have built or extended their oeuvres to include an analysis of environmental problems, has criminology seen fit *not* to do so? Alternatively, why are there so few criminologists writing about environmental harm/crime, as opposed to the multitude prepared to discuss such issues as illicit drug taking, rape, robbery, homicide and other so-called "orthodox" crimes?'
3	Green criminology is a 'niche area where its focus renders it of little interest to mainstream criminology's more established notions' of the problem of crime (Potter, 2013: 131–132).	The focus on harm is a well-established notion within criminology, and zemiology is a well-respected discipline. Green criminology is ultimately a form of both criminology and zemiology, as it enables the consideration of both harm and crime.
4	Due to 'the overt taking of sides – green criminology is manifestly *not* value-free, and therefore undermines the ideals of a social *science*' (Potter, 2013: 132, emphasis in original).	Social science incorporates quantitative, qualitative, and mixed method epistemological approaches, all of which are laden with benefits and limitations (see: Bryman, 2016). Whilst much green criminological research is of a qualitative nature (Lynch et al., 2017), some green criminologists do undertake quantitative research which conforms to Potter's (2013) notion of traditional, objective, and scientific, social science. For examples of quantitative green criminology, see: Lynch and Pires (2019).

However, there is a further limitation to green criminology which is significant to the main aim of this book. This is the thought that, due to the diverse nature and breadth of green criminology, those operating within the perspective generally only offer bespoke solutions to the individual environmental harms and crimes that are identified. It must be noted that there is great value in offering such unique solutions. For example, an increase in wildlife enforcement has been offered as one solution to combat and reduce illicit trades in flora and fauna (Kretser et al., 2015; Wyatt, 2013: 314). However, despite such pivotal work, such unique solutions are clearly not applicable for all environmental harms. Therefore, it can be argued that green criminology has lacked a broader, holistic solution to the environmental harms that have been identified.

Some universal solutions do exist within green criminology. Stretesky et al. (2014), for example, purport that the ToP is responsible for a vast array of environmental harms and that the structural inequalities inherent within the capitalist mode of production disproportionately impact the most vulnerable people, societies, and natural environments. Therefore, for Stretesky et al. (2014), changes in the ToP would represent a holistic solution to environmental harms. The main problem with this argument is that such change is thwarted by important state–corporate relationships which together ensure the necessary changes cannot be made (Lampkin, 2018).

ToP theory considers structural issues and inequalities within society and is hyper-critical of the role corporations play in creating environmental harm. Conversely, ordinary and everyday acts that are environmentally harmful (such as driving a petrol car or not recycling) have also been stated as a green criminological problem with a holistic solution. It has been suggested that such individual acts – *taken together* on a mass scale – contribute to ecocide (Agnew, 2013). Viewing environmental harm in this two-dimensional way (ToP and individual acts) enables two contrasting (yet still holistic) solutions to be identified. With regards to the ToP, the answer lies in structural transformation. For individual environmental harms, the solution can be found in doing more to reduce our own individual contribution, therefore reducing the impact of environmental harms committed 'en masse' (Halsey and White, 1998: 347).

The final holistic solution currently entertained by green criminologists is that of ecophilosophy (Halsey and White, 1998; Lampkin, 2018: 88–98; White, 2008a: 10–14; Wyatt, 2013). This concept suggests that there are three highly juxtaposing positions from which to view environmental harms and crimes: anthropocentrism, biocentrism, and ecocentrism. According to Halsey and White (1998: 349, emphasis in original), anthropocentrism leads to intense environmental degradation because non-human nature is 'viewed *instrumentally* – as something to be appropriated, processed, consumed, and disposed of in a manner which best suits the immediate interests of human beings.' Under anthropocentrism, then, laws are designed to encourage the exploitation and commodification of natural resources in ways that best ensure the enjoyment of human life. Conversely, biocentrism conceives 'human beings as simply another species to be attributed the *same* moral worth as' other organisms (Halsey and White, 1998: 352, emphasis in original). Under such a perspective, laws would be contrived with the natural world at the forefront of debate and decision making, and as a result, environmentally harmful practices would be curtailed (or even eradicated) in order to preserve the ecological health of the planet. The final ecophilosophy, ecocentrism, entertains a sphere equidistant between anthropocentrism and biocentrism. Ecocentrism recognises the unique and privileged position and capacity of human beings to 'develop and deploy methods of production which have global consequences' (Halsey and White, 1998: 355). Therefore, an ecocentric approach to lawmaking would 'ensure that such production methods do not exceed the ecospheric limits of the planet' (Halsey and White, 1998: 35).

Therefore, ecophilosophy, ToP theory, and ecocide are three examples of how green criminology has attempted to provide more holistic explanations and solutions to environmental harms and crimes.

2.6. Conclusion

Ecophilosophy is extremely important to this book – *Uniting Green Criminology and Earth Jurisprudence* – because it provides a unique cross-over between the two disciplines, as both green criminologists (Halsey and White, 1998; Lampkin, 2018: 88–98; White, 2008a: 10–14; Wyatt, 2013) and those writing and researching within earth jurisprudence (Burdon, 2011a; Damtie, 2011) have discussed the importance of anthropocentrism, biocentrism, and ecocentrism. However, they were not the first disciplines to analyse ecophilosophy. Lampkin (2018: 87) suggests that these are already 'well-established principles in the environmental philosophy and environmental ethics arenas,' respectively, a theme also identified by Halsey and White (1998; for more insight into anthropocentrism, see the work of: Gagnon Thompson and Burton (1994) and Nash (1989); for biocentrism see: Sterba (2011) and Watson (1983); and for ecocentrism see: Merchant (1990).

Ecophilosophy is important because the vantage point of biocentrism suggests that the earth – and all the natural human and ecological components within – should be placed at the forefront of human laws and decision making. After all, Wyatt (2013: 62) suggests that one of the disadvantages of the anthropocentric approach is that it is:

> so focused on short-term gain that the eventual damage to human livelihoods and health caused by overexploitation is not recognised or acknowledged. Human profits and well-being are threatened in direct

> contradiction to the aim of an anthropocentric approach, yet in not understanding the interconnectedness of people to the environment, destructive behaviours continue unquestioned.

This biocentric approach strikes a clear parallel with wild law and earth jurisprudence. As Cullinan (2011a: 13) suggests when discussing its basic principles:

> earth jurisprudence is a philosophy of law and human governance that is based on the idea that humans are only one part of a wider community of beings and that the welfare of that community is dependent on the welfare of the earth as a whole.

The basic premise of this book is that earth jurisprudence and biocentric approaches to lawmaking can act as a useful, holistic solution to the multitude of environmental harms exposed by green criminologists. This connection (between earth jurisprudence and green criminology) has not been made before. As a result, the remainder of this book will focus firstly on mapping the contours of wild law and earth jurisprudence (Chapter 3) before moving on to make a unique theoretical contribution to knowledge and theory (Chapter 4). This contribution involves a discussion of how green criminology can benefit from utilising the principles of earth jurisprudence and what earth jurisprudence (as a discipline) can gain from collaborating with green criminologists. It is hoped that doing this will foster new theoretical debates and contributions in these areas (green criminology and wild law), thus broadening the theoretical horizons of both disciplines.

3 Historical and theoretical foundations of an earth jurisprudence

> A meaningful response to the ecological and social challenges of this era requires a shift of thinking at the jurisprudential level.
>
> (Koons, 2012: 351)

3.1. Introduction

Chapter 2 identified the historical and theoretical foundations of green criminology, providing critique of the term 'green' and discussing the advantages and limitations of having a 'green' criminology. Chapter 3 will follow a similar path but apply such discussions to earth jurisprudence and wild law. Understanding the historical and theoretical foundations of both green criminology and wild law acts as the necessary starting point for forging initial arguments as to why it is beneficial to unite these disciplines. Doing so will provide a solution to many anthropocentric environmental harms and crimes. Whilst it is recognised that there are fundamental problems with such a solution (see Section 3.3., 'A critique of wild law and earth jurisprudence'), the arguments are placed in the context of the whole host of benefits that could be achieved by urging collaboration between the two disciplines (Chapter 4). However, before we move on to discussions of a potential partnership, it is imperative to understand the historical and theoretical foundations of earth jurisprudence and wild law. This will be done by considering what the terms 'earth jurisprudence' and 'wild law' mean (Section 3.2.); critiquing wild law and earth jurisprudence (Section 3.3.); analysing the similarities and differences between the theoretical and conceptual underpinnings of earth jurisprudence and green criminology (Section 3.4.); and analysing case studies and success stories of the incorporation of earth jurisprudential principles into human-made laws in different parts of the world (Section 3.5.) such as New Zealand, Bolivia, and Ecuador.

3.2. What is 'earth jurisprudence' and what is 'wild law'? Historical and theoretical foundations

As you will be aware by now (due to my doing so in this book), the lexical terms 'earth jurisprudence' and 'wild law' are frequently employed interchangeably. Whilst their meanings are analogous, the terms do essentially refer to different things, so defining and differentiating their meaning is a natural starting point to this chapter.

Wild law, then, refers to 'formal law founded on principles of earth jurisprudence' (Mason, 2011: 41), whilst earth jurisprudence 'is a philosophy of law that applies . . . (the) intimate understanding of nature to modern human law-making' (Mason, 2011: 36). Therefore, when the term 'wild law' is expressed (in this book and by other authors writing about wild law and earth jurisprudence), it is referring to laws made by humans but constructed according to the principles of the philosophy of earth jurisprudence. Consequently, earth jurisprudence can be understood as a particular approach to thinking about the relationship between the earth (and all the ecological systems contained within) and human lawmaking. Furthermore – and similar to green criminology – earth jurisprudence can be understood as not just one unitary theory but a set of perspectives and approaches to the philosophy of law, with the earth-system privileged within these approaches. The remainder of this chapter will discuss in more detail some of these approaches and perspectives.

To make the differentiation between wild law and earth jurisprudence easier to understand, Table 3.1 provides a list of five principles of earth jurisprudence devised by Cullinan (2011a: 13).

The philosophy of lawmaking under wild law and earth jurisprudence represents an ecocentric approach whereby the axiology of everything in the universe (including earth, humans, and the wider ecology or – as Cullinan describes – earth community, encompassing, plants, animals, humans, and the natural environment more broadly) is the same. In other words, everything in the universe has – and should be treated as having – the same value and moral standing. With respect to the conceptual similarities between earth jurisprudence and ecocentrism (and ecophilosophy more generally), Koons (2011: 45) 'recognises a kinship' between earth jurisprudence and 'the field of environmental ethics,' much the same as the connexion between green criminology and ecophilosophy (Halsey and White, 1998).

This way of thinking typifies one of the central theoretical underpinnings of the philosophy of earth jurisprudence – *wholeness* (Mason, 2011: 36, emphasis added). There is a recognition here that everything is connected, that each individual member of the earth community (i.e. a human or a bird or an earthworm) plays a vital part in the sustenance and existence of the entire earth community. This is represented in Principles Four and Five of

Table 3.1 Principles of Earth Jurisprudence

Principle	*Description*
1	'The Universe is the primary law-giver, not human legal systems' (Cullinan, 2011a: 13).
2	All members of the earth community 'have fundamental "rights," including the right to exist, to habitat or a place to be, and to participate in the evolution of the earth community' (Cullinan, 2011a: 13).
3	'The rights of each being are limited by the rights of other beings to the extent necessary to maintain the integrity, balance and health of the communities within which it exists' (Cullinan, 2011a: 13).
4	'Human acts or laws that infringe these fundamental rights violate the fundamental relationships and principles that constitute the earth community ("the great jurisprudence") and are consequently illegitimate and unlawful' (Cullinan, 2011a: 13).
5	'Humans must adapt their legal, political, economic and social systems to be consistent with the Great Jurisprudence . . . which means that human governance systems at all times take account of the interests of the whole earth community and must: • determine the lawfulness of human conduct by whether or not it strengthens or weakens the relationships that constitute the earth community; • maintain a dynamic balance between the rights of humans and those of other members of the earth community on the basis of what is best for the earth as a whole; • promote restorative justice . . . rather than punishment . . . ; • recognise all members of the earth community as subjects before the law, with the right to the protection of the law' (Cullinan, 2011a: 13).

Cullinan's (2011a) work when he refers to the 'great jurisprudence.' Cullinan (2011a) has adopted this term from what is often called the first body of writing on earth jurisprudence completed by Thomas Berry (1999). In this text, Berry (1999) describes how a new approach to lawmaking could act as the great work of a generation, that being, changing our (human) jurisprudential approach to the legal, economic, political, and social relationships with the natural world. For Berry (1999: 74), 'only a jurisprudence based on concern for an integral earth community is capable of sustaining a viable planet.'

Whilst Berry's (1999) *great work* is often regarded as the first text deliberating earth jurisprudence, it was by no means the founding literature linking how we (as humans) conceive of our relationship with the natural world. As mentioned in Chapter 2, the arena of environmental ethics preceded green criminology, and so too it preceded earth jurisprudence and wild law. As

Mason (2011: 37) suggests, 'the philosophic foundations for such respect for nature are not new' to earth jurisprudence. Koons (2011: 46) notes how such thinking has pre-occupied the minds of many people for decades, including 'environmental reformers, social justice activists, indigenous rights movements, and grassroots campaigns for sustainability.' Similarly, Schillmoller and Pelizzon (2013) root their criticism of earth jurisprudence in the much earlier work of deep ecology and political ecology.

As a result, earth jurisprudence can be viewed as an extension of earlier thinking within environmental ethics disciplines. However, what separates earth jurisprudence from environmental ethics is its continual focus on jurisprudence – the philosophy of law – and how humans could shift their thinking (in theory and in practice) from human-centred conceptions of lawmaking to earth-centred ones. Such thinking is very closely aligned with biocentric ecophilosophy. However, earth jurisprudence avoids the polarisation between anthropocentrism and biocentrism by continuing to focus on the important role of humans in shaping the protection of the environment through wild law. As Koons (2012: 368) suggests, 'the proper role of systems of law and governance is not to regulate the environment, but for humanity to regulate itself for the good of the earth community.'

To conclude this section, it is worth noting that the principles of earth jurisprudence identified by Cullinan (2011a) in Table 3.1 are just one person's interpretation of some key underlying principles of the philosophy. They were utilised in this chapter to give the reader a comprehensive picture and understanding of what constitutes some key thinking within earth jurisprudence. However, a number of other authors have attempted to 'map the terrain' of earth jurisprudence (see: Bell, 2003; Burdon, 2011b; Koons, 2008, 2009, 2011, 2012; Mason, 2011; Schillmoller and Pelizzon, 2013), and it is worthwhile critiquing some of this material within this section (dedicated to the historical and theoretical foundations of earth jurisprudence). I have decided to focus on the seminal work of Koons (2009, 2011) and Bell (2003), who were some of the first scholars to establish key principles for earth jurisprudence following Berry's (1999) call to re-think our approach to jurisprudence.

Koon's (2009, 2011: 45–54) influential work sketched a vision of three essential guiding principles for earth jurisprudence: the intrinsic value of the earth (subjectivity); the relational responsibility of humanity toward earth (communion); and the democratic governance of the earth community (differentiation). These three principles were created by Berry (1999: 162) and expanded on by Bell (2003: 90–92) but given a greater degree of conceptualisation by Koons (2009, 2011: 45–54). Each of these three principles will now be discussed in turn.

The intrinsic value of the earth essentially refers to the earth being a part of – and subject to – the fundamental laws of the universe (for example:

gravity, thermodynamics, relativity, etc.). This means that the earth is a self-organising system that is constantly reacting to the laws of the universe of which it is unavoidably a part. For Koons (2011: 47), recognising and understanding this intrinsic value 'carries legal, philosophical, and moral significance' and, when applied to earth jurisprudence, affects both humans and non-human nature uniformly. This is because both forms (humans and non-humans) are subject to the same basic laws that govern the universe and – therefore – warrant equal '*moral consideration*' (Koons, 2011: 48, emphasis in original). The intrinsic value of the cosmos, the earth, humans, and non-humans means that everything has the same moral worth because they are part of and subject to the same universal laws. Under this notion, there is nothing particularly special about humans other than the fact that they occupy a space within the community of the cosmos.

Koons's (2009, 2011) second fundamental principle of earth jurisprudence refers to the *relational responsibility* of humanity toward the earth (also referred to as the *communion*) and is essentially a development of the first principle (of intrinsic value). The argument here is that all the matter in the cosmos is related from the very first moments of existence and reality (the big bang). As a result, 'each particle has been related to every other particle in the universe' since this initial beginning (Koons, 2011: 47). Therefore, everything in the universe is deemed to be related and, consequently, the moral worth of all particles is the same (regardless of humanity, sentience, thoughts, feelings, and meaningful constructions). The ontological reality of everything is the same, because all matter shares the identical basic standard of being created following the big bang.

The democratic governance of the earth community is Koon's (2009, 2011) third and final principle underlining earth jurisprudence. This principle refers to the philosophy of governance and legal systems on earth. Koons (2011: 53) denotes how these systems are currently articulated as 'of the people, by the people and for the people' (at least in the majority of Western democratic nations). Under earth jurisprudence, governance and legal systems would operate in a democratic fashion and with a primacy on the welfare of the whole earth community (due to the interrelatedness and equal moral value of all things – as expressed in Koons's first two principles). As a result, this would create governance and legal systems *of the earth community, by the (human members of) the earth community, and for the earth community.*

The structure of Bell's (2003) quintessential article was very different from that of Koons, which probably represents the nascent stage of earth jurisprudence at the time he was writing. Bell's (2003) text was an exploratory investigation into Thomas Berry's work on earth jurisprudence specifically designed to pose questions and postulate answers to some fundamental preliminary issues. Furthermore, Bell (2003: 69) actively sought to encourage and foster further debate into earth jurisprudence owing to the fact that readers were 'invited to respond directly' to the essay via a corresponding discussion forum.

One of Bell's (2003: 90) predictions with regard to earth jurisprudence was that it would develop over time and the transition from a human to an earth jurisprudence would be a slow one. Bell (2003: 90) described this as a logical analogy because it would take more and more 'individuals and groups around the world' to 'become concerned (enough) about the devastation of' the planet 'to press for action.' Therefore, a transition to an earth jurisprudence would not be an immediate reality. According to Bell (2003: 90):

> Our level of consciousness will increase. For periods of time there will be two parallel jurisprudences existing together, running side by side, one of them a human jurisprudence, the other, an alternative system – an Earth jurisprudence. Periodically they may fly further apart; at other times they may come closer together. There will be moments of grace when a sort of integration takes place and the rights of the other-than-human species begin to be recognized within the human-jurisprudence systems. As the situation on our planet becomes more desperate, the two systems may begin to merge or at least establish a more permanent symbiotic relationship. We will become more and more part of the Earth jurisprudence system; it will become more and more part of us.

Bell's (2003) work was influential because it recognised earth jurisprudence as an emerging philosophy, giving greater conceptualisation to the discipline than Berry's (1999) initial outline and reasoning behind the need for an earth jurisprudence.

Now that the historical and theoretical underpinnings of an earth jurisprudence have been discussed, the next section will provide a critique of earth jurisprudence in order to understand the strengths and limitations of the discipline in greater detail. Understanding earth jurisprudence in this way will enable comparisons to be made with green criminology (in Section 3.4.), which in turn will lay the foundation for discussing both disciplines simultaneously in Chapter 4 ('Uniting green criminology and earth jurisprudence').

3.3. A critique of wild law and earth jurisprudence

The main advantage of utilising an earth jurisprudence approach is that it tackles anthropocentrically induced environmental degradation from the heart of lawmaking. One of the central arguments is that a radically different earth-centred approach to making and administering the law will result in decreased environmental degradation because the needs of the whole earth community will be prioritised over the material and economic needs of humans (the latter being the current state of affairs as we enter the Anthropocene). The previous section highlighted the work of Bell (2003), who envisioned that transition from human-centred to earth-centred governance and legal systems would be a slow-process in which earth jurisprudential principles are embedded within human legal systems *over time* – as a means of addressing environmental degradation.

Whilst such an approach is clearly thought provoking (and is certainly a potential solution to widespread environmental harms), there are several problems with adopting and implementing wild law in practice (Lampkin and Wyatt, 2019). This section (3.3.) will identify some of these difficulties by providing a thorough critique of earth jurisprudence. The main problems are highlighted in Table 3.2 at the end of this section.

The first critique is that earth jurisprudence is not proposing anything particularly new (Koons, 2011). Implementing an earth-centred approach into lawmaking is a well-founded concept that has been discussed at length within the biocentric ecosophy. To give an example, Halsey and White (1998) – writing before Berry (1999) – proposed that a jurisprudential change to human legal systems described how anthropocentric, ecocentric and biocentric perspectives and approaches to lawmaking and enforcement would change the relationship between humans and the natural world. They used the example of the clear-felling of old-growth forests in Australia to discuss these ideas. They proposed that, under an anthropocentric perspective, 'old growth forests are viewed instrumentally . . . as a means to satisfy the demands of *human* beings' and would therefore be 'exploited for their commercial potential' using production methods 'which incur the least cost to producers' (Halsey and White, 1998: 360–361, emphasis in original). As a result, the seminal 'aim of legislation is to 'facilitate the extraction process' and to ensure that 'human production and consumption is . . . privileged over long-term ecosystemic well-being' (Halsey and White, 1998: 362, see also: White, 2008a: 12). Contrariwise, under a biocentric perspective, old-growth forests are deemed to have 'intrinsic worth' with ecological 'significance independent of any value placed on them by human beings' (Halsey and White, 1998: 363). Consequently, 'regulatory legislation should be directed first and foremost to preserving the natural environment' because humans 'are simply one of a multitude of species, and they do not have an ethical right to engage in activities which are destructive of natural habitats and ecosystems' (Halsey and White, 1998: 364). Amidst anthropocentrism and biocentrism is ecocentrism. Here, regarding the felling of old-growth forests, the regulatory concern is to 'ensure that a balance is achieved between human needs and ecological health' (Halsey and White, 1998: 366), effectively representing a middle ground between anthropocentric and biocentric perspectives. It is clear to see, then, that a biocentric approach (which considers humans as simply another species) adopts the same approach to lawmaking as wild law and earth jurisprudence.

Secondly, it is undeniable that 21st-century human legal systems prioritise the economic and social needs of humans over those of the natural world. As has previously been stated, human laws are constructed 'of the people, by the people and for the people' (Koons, 2011: 53), rather than of, by, and for the earth community as a whole. Therefore, by proposing the full incorporation of the natural world as the primary concern for lawmakers, earth jurisprudential advocates are suggesting a complete (and very radical) shift from how humans currently make law to how they *should* make law. Whilst Bell (2003) concedes that this will be a slow process, less has been written about how this transition will actually take place and the several barriers that exist preventing such a radical jurisprudential shift. As a result, earth jurisprudential theorists can be seen to (thus far) provide heavy support and rationale for *why* a shift in thinking is pivotal (i.e. the current inexorable anthropocentric destruction of the earth's ecosystems and natural resources) rather than tackling the complexities surrounding *how* this shift would unfold in practice considering the vastly different jurisprudential approach to lawmaking that currently permeates human legal systems. As Rogers (2017: 2, in: Lampkin and Wyatt, 2019: 10–11) contemplates:

> How do we interpret or deconstruct our existing law/laws wildly, such that humanity is not necessarily the primary focus? How do we disregard our own self-interest, our ingrained assumptions and presuppositions as part of the human species, and indeed as part of a particular subset of the human species, to prioritise or at least recognise and respect Earth and its many communities and lifeforms in the process of wildly rewriting law?

With this in mind, it may be impossible to fully integrate an earth jurisprudence into human ways of constructing and making law, particularly under a global capitalist economy that prioritises wealth and economic growth. Scholars within green criminology refer to this state of affairs as the ToP (Lynch et al., 2013; Stretesky et al., 2014), whereby environmental harms and crimes are regarded as a consequence of political–economic relationships between the state, lawmakers, and large corporations. Such actors are entrenched within this system and are reliant upon these relationships in order to function effectively. It is therefore arguable that a fully earth-centred jurisprudential transition would be impossible due to these political–economic relationships which would undoubtedly resist such change (as it contradicts their motives and essential ways of operating). Therefore, a complete transformation in the global political economy would be an essential component to facilitating and embedding earth jurisprudence within human-made law – which may be an unrealistic, overly ambitious, or even impossible machination. These themes are highlighted by Lampkin and Wyatt (2019: 10) when they state that:

> Such a radical change to society is, of course, fraught with obstacles, both political and practical. We suspect that states and corporations, in particular, would oppose such changes as they challenge several aspects of their existence. First, an Earth-centric society with a legal infrastructure protecting the whole Earth community would disrupt markets and industries as they currently function. Corporations would not want this to happen as it may impact (decrease) their profits.

A further critique of earth jurisprudence can be made in light of the focus of the discipline on the premise of *sustainability*. Koons (2012: 369), for example, suggests that 'if a system of law and governance were to honour differentiation, the principle of sustainability would be given primacy to safeguard the diversity of life for present and future generations.' Whilst the principle of sustainability is undeniably a central facet to many environmental laws and international agreements (i.e. the 2015 Paris Climate Agreement), it can be argued that adopting sustainability as a central feature of earth jurisprudence is inherently flawed due to the exploitation and mis-use of the term by corporations (mirroring the argument made in Chapter 2 concerning Halsey's (2013) *branding* issues). For example, when analysing the intersection of sustainability, environmental harm, and the First Nations people of Alberta, Canada, Heydon (2018, 2019) recognises how the term 'sustainable development' has been used as a justification for the provincial government of Alberta to allow the rapid extraction of natural resources in that area, creating incredible environmental harm and cultural loss. As Heydon (2019: 15) suggests:

> 'the sustainable development' of the oil sands has been a strategic objective of the provincial government since the mid-1990s, when rapid expansion of the industry began. As such, there is a need to explain how and why industrial development has been consistently permitted under this rubric despite very clear and credible evidence that it is anything but 'sustainable.'

Therefore, earth jurisprudence advocates need to ensure that such terms are adequately and thoroughly defined and debated before they are applied as gospel principles underlining the discipline, as this could taint future development.

One of the greatest critiques of earth jurisprudence comes from 'the incommensurability between a theory of earth justice and practice of an earth justice system,' which, it has been suggested, 'will continue to involve exponents of earth jurisprudence in a host of scientific, legal, political and ethical tensions' (Schillmoller and Pelizzon, 2013: 1–2). As has already been suggested, it may not even be possible to transfer the emerging philosophy of earth jurisprudence into law because of the powerful political–economic relationships that manifest between corporations and those politicians and practitioners who make the law. Whilst a fundamental notion within earth jurisprudence suggests that human laws can transform into becoming earth-centred once it is recognised that humans are just one part of the earth community (Cullinan, 2011a: 13), it is unclear how humans are to achieve this visualisation in practice. One explanation for this is provided by Bell (2003: 77), who states that:

> unlike a human jurisprudence, an Earth jurisprudence is not a human creation, it is not something that is man-made. Rather, like the spirit of the bear in the soap stone, it is 'natural,' something that already exists in nature. An Earth jurisprudence is implicit in the laws of nature.

Therefore, Bell (2003) is suggesting that earth jurisprudence already exists as a naturally occurring mechanism implicit in the laws of nature, but it is clear that this is not how humans are currently operating due to the ubiquitous anthropocentric environmental harms that exist even despite the laws and regulations that are designed to curb and prevent such harm. As a result, it is difficult to see how humans can simply 'realise' earth jurisprudence and put this concept into practice. These themes are debated by Schillmoller and Pelizzon (2013: 24), who suggest that 'because a human jurisprudence is a system of laws designed to recognise the pre-eminence of the human species, it is unlikely that a human jurisprudence can serve as a suitable framework for an earth jurisprudence.' However, it must be noted that this type of critique is a fairly negative and defeatist way of viewing earth jurisprudence and its future. Earth jurisprudence is very much in its infancy, and answers to these conundrums may be provided by future scholars writing and researching in the area of earth jurisprudence.

Another critique of earth jurisprudence rests in the stark differences between humans and non-humans. The goal of earth jurisprudence is to recognise humans as part of the wider ecological makeup of planet Earth (and even of the cosmos) of which we are inevitably entrenched within. This means that humans should be treated the same as non-human animals and ecosystems because of a shared value and moral worth. As Koons (2008: 338) suggests, humankind is 'an intimately connected part of a greater whole . . . (therefore), humanity must not claim moral status for ourselves, while denying it to the rest of the community in which we are embedded.' As a result, recognising 'the interconnectedness of the earth community mandates the widening of the moral community' (Koons, 2008: 338). Despite these arguments, it is clear that earth jurisprudence seeks to shift legal systems created by and for humans to one that recognises all entities equally. Therefore, several questions arise from this premise (for more discussion, see Schillmoller and Pelizzon, 2013: 13–14). If an earth-centred jurisprudence is to represent the voices of non-human nature in an equal capacity as humans, who is to speak and represent those non-human entities (such as rivers, seas, non-human animals, flora, and fauna) in a court of law? Can a human adequately represent a non-human entity in a way that adequately fulfils the needs of that entity? How can a human fully understand (let alone respect and represent) the needs of non-human entities of which he or she has never experienced (due to their very characteristic of being human)? Questions on the voice and representation of non-humans within anthropocentric legal systems has been highly contested by many scholars across multiple disciplines and particularly within environmental ethics (Donoso, 2017; Eckersley, 2011). Earth jurisprudence has not yet agreed on concrete answers to these puzzling questions, which may be partly due to the infancy of the philosophy.

A final critique of earth jurisprudence concerns the idea of environmental rights. When Berry (1999) devised his initial text on earth jurisprudence, he was very clear that 'rights' for nature should be one of the key principles of earth jurisprudence (see also: Berry, 2011) – that all living things should have rights. Whilst the concept of rights for nature has drawn much academic attention (Nash, 1989; Turner, 2013a, 2013b) – as a method of protecting the earth from environmental harm – there are two major issues with embedding the rights of nature within earth jurisprudence. First is the previously stated issue of how nature and non-human entities are adequately and accurately represented within a human-created legal system. Secondly, there is no guarantee that successfully creating environmental rights will lead to the abolition of environmental harm and the cessation of environmental degradation (Birnbacher, 1998) – or that such rights will not be voided by future humans (McGrory Klyza, 1994; Woods, 2006: 582). Whilst it is likely that rights for nature would go some way to minimising environmental harm by providing legal systems with the necessary framework for criminalising acts that breach environmental rights (Birnbacher, 1998), the issues of significant political-economic relationships identified so far (particularly in relation to the ToP and treadmill of crime, see: Stretesky et al., 2014) means that there is a disjuncture between environmental rights in theory and the success of implementing the rights of nature in practice. After all, the creation of human rights following the atrocities of World War II has not resulted in the protection of all humans from harms. Breaches of human rights are ubiquitous across all societies despite the implementation of such rights in domestic and international law.

To conclude, Table 3.2 demonstrates a summary of the six key criticisms of wild law and earth jurisprudence as discussed in this section.

The criticisms outlined in this section highlight the need for further theoretical contemplation of earth jurisprudence. Solving these conundrums will enable human legal systems to begin to steer towards a more earth-centred jurisprudence and prevent earth jurisprudence as a discipline from being (to take a phrase from Schillmoller and Pelizzon, 2013: 14) 'trapped in a realm of ideas,' without Berry's (1999) *Great Work* having ever been achieved.

The next section (3.4.) will proceed from critiquing earth jurisprudence and move on to discussing the similarities and differences between the discipline and green criminology. Doing this (thinking of both subjects in unison) will provide a useful platform from which to discuss the potential collaboration of the two disciplines in Chapter 4 ('Uniting green criminology and earth jurisprudence').

Table 3.2 Six Major Criticisms of Earth Jurisprudence

Argument No.	*Critique*	*Reference/Further Information*
1	The principles of earth jurisprudence are not new. Incorporating earth-centred principles into human-centred legal systems has been debated in environmental ethics and closely mirrors arguments within biocentrism.	Halsey and White (1998); Koons (2011: 45–46)
2	Earth jurisprudence requires a radical shift in human legal systems from what is currently practiced in much of the Western world. Earth jurisprudence scholars have not yet shed much light on how this shift would take place in practice. Furthermore, ToP theory would argue it is impossible to undertake this shift due to the inherent power dynamics and inequalities prevalent in the major economies and nations of the world.	Lampkin and Wyatt (2019); Schillmoller and Pelizzon (2013); Stretesky et al. (2014)
3	The focus on sustainability within earth jurisprudence is contradictory because utilising such principles can still lead to considerable environmental harm.	Heydon (2019); Koons (2012)
4	There exists an incommensurability between earth jurisprudential theory and wild law in practice. There are only a handful of examples of how earth jurisprudence has been incorporated into human-made law.	Schillmoller and Pelizzon (2013)

Argument No.	*Critique*	*Reference/Further Information*
5	It is unclear how non-human entities are to have a voice within an inescapably human legal system. Who is the right 'person' to represent non-human entities? Is their perception inevitably tainted by their being human?	Donoso (2017); Eckersley (2011); Rogers (2017: 2, in: Lampkin and Wyatt, 2019: 10–11)
6	Earth jurisprudence places great weight on the rights of nature, but these are unclear. How is one to achieve the implementation of environmental rights? And is there any guarantee that this will lead to the cessation of environmental degradation?	Birnbacher (1998); Nash (1989); Turner (2013a, 2013b)

3.4. Conceptualising the similarities and differences between earth jurisprudence and green criminology

One of the main similarities between earth jurisprudence and green criminology is that they are both off-shoots of their larger parent disciplines (law and criminology, respectively). Furthermore, both sub-disciplines emerged in the late 20th century as a result of a perceived failure of law and criminology to deal effectively with environmental harms and crimes. For example, when considering the emergence of green criminology, Stretesky et al. (2014: 1) suggest that:

> A concerted effort to draw criminological attention to environmental harm emerged within criminology in 1990 when Lynch issued a call for 'green criminology.' According to Lynch, the study of crime failed to account for the tremendous amount of environmental harm that was occurring. Specifically, Lynch observed that criminologists failed to explain ecological destruction because they omitted social economic factors that shaped laws and power relations, and instead relied on the narrow definition of crime contained within the criminal law.

Therefore, green criminology can be seen to have developed from the perceived failings of criminology to move beyond the secular notion of crime but also as a means to address increasingly more common and severe forms of global environmental harm. The emergence of an earth jurisprudence mirrors that of green criminology in these two important aspects. When discussing the impetuses for delegate participation in Australia's first conference on wild law in 2009, Burdon (2010: 62) recognises that 'all 63 participants were motivated by a shared view that our current system of law and governance was failing to protect the natural world from destruction and were seeking a new path forward.'

However, whilst both earth jurisprudence and green criminology can be seen as new and emerging fields, both dissatisfied with current legal and criminological responses to environmental harm, there exists a key difference between the two subjects which may account for the continued successes and experimentation within green criminology, in stark contrast to the slowly evolving discipline of earth jurisprudence. This key difference manifests itself in the way each discipline is conceived theoretically. For example, the commonly cited perception is that green criminology is considered as a perspective (South, 1998) rather than a distinct criminological theory. As a result, green criminology has attracted a range of academics to conducting research and theoretical work under green criminology's conceptual umbrella due to the fact that the broad, all-encompassing nature of the perspective allows for a range of issues concerning environmental harm and crime to be discussed. Green criminology is not therefore restricted by time, space, or the type of environmental harm under scrutiny. This approach has allowed green criminology to blossom in the last twenty years.

Conversely, earth jurisprudence can be seen to be restricted by its narrow focus on law and rights (in comparison to the breadth of green criminological debate encompassing both crime and harm). It is worth reiterating here that wild law refers to 'formal law founded on principles of earth jurisprudence' (Mason, 2011: 41), whilst earth jurisprudence 'is a philosophy of law that applies . . . [the] intimate understanding of nature to modern human law-making' (Mason, 2011: 36). Therefore, the fact that earth jurisprudence is a philosophy grounded within the specific focus on wild law – how laws are (or should be) made – is a contributing factor to the lack of academic scholarship within earth jurisprudence in contrast to green criminology.

Despite this, green criminology certainly has something to learn from earth jurisprudence, a theme that will be discussed in considerable detail in Chapter 4. Whilst the focus of earth jurisprudence is law, green criminology could be criticised as focusing too heavily on law enforcement as a method of 'resolving' environmental harms. In this way, green criminology can be seen to be *reactive*, responding to harms that have already taken place, rather than *preventative*, seeking solutions to the cessation of future environmental harms.

Despite such perceived differences, there are two key, additional similarities between earth jurisprudence and green criminology. Firstly, both disciplines emerged out of the perceived social and ecological injustices exhibited in contemporary society. Just the same way that green criminology for Lynch (1990), was the coming together of at least three movements – ecofeminism, environmental racism, and ecological socialisms (Hall, 2013: 5–6) – earth jurisprudence too 'embraces the connection between Earth justice and social justice' (Koons, 2011: 45). As a result, both disciplines can be seen as radical and critical offshoots of their parent discipline. Secondly, both earth jurisprudence and green criminology are accepting of both critique and collaboration from scholars both *inside* and *outside* their disciplines. Whilst this undoubtedly allows for the development of both disciplines, which is important in their early stages, Schillmoller and Pelizzon (2013: 8) have discussed how such a collaborative philosophy could prevent earth jurisprudence from generating a 'stable and non-negotiable landscape' (which is arguably imperative for a discipline founded on the premise that laws need to change to reflect the earth jurisprudence philosophy). As Schillmoller and Pelizzon (2013: 7–8) discuss:

> As a transdisciplinary endeavour, the development of frameworks for earth jurisprudence will be informed by a range of disciplinary paradigms including those of law, philosophy and the social, natural and biological sciences. But because each discipline employs different historically and culturally specific methods of knowledge production, any attempt to arrive at a coherent and unified framework for Earth jurisprudence would risk misrepresenting the richness and complexity of its conceptual terrain. Consequently, recognition that knowledge production is variable across paradigmatic divides renders problematic the identification of a stable and non-negotiable landscape for an earth justice system.

As has been highlighted in this chapter so far, the philosophy of earth jurisprudence is very much in its infancy – a concept developed by Berry (1999) in his influential text entitled *The Great Work*. Whilst the birth of earth jurisprudence as a discipline, then, emerged at a similar time to Lynch's (1990) call for a 'green' criminology, there is a comparably small number of academics writing within the earth jurisprudence discipline in contrast to the growing mass of primary research and theoretical scholarship in the perspective of green criminology. As a result, earth jurisprudence has been described as in a 'nascent stage' (Schillmoller and Pelizzon, 2013: 7) and is only just beginning to expose itself as a legitimate and valuable discipline within its own right. As a result, there is remarkably little work defining, debating, and theorising the key principles of an earth jurisprudence and very few examples of wild law and earth jurisprudential principles in practice. However, some examples do exist, and the significance of these will now be discussed in greater detail.

3.5. Case studies and success stories: earth jurisprudence in practice?

In order to discuss the viability of an earth jurisprudence in practice, it is essential to discuss historic success stories – examples of how wild law and earth jurisprudence (or at least their philosophies and earth-centred approaches) have been enshrined within various legal endeavours. These could include domestic and international regulations, legislations and agreements, constitutional embedment, and human or non-human 'rights.' In this regard, this section will briefly draw upon three case studies as examples. These include, firstly, the legal recognition of the Whanganui River (New Zealand) as a legal person with 'rights of its own equivalent to human rights' (Hsiao, 2012: 371). The second is the adoption of the rights of nature, or *Pacha Mama*, into the Ecuadorian Constitution in 2008 (Espinosa, 2019). And the third is the rights of nature that were entrenched within two Bolivian statutes in 2010 and 2012 (Calzadilla and Kotzé, 2018).

Legal personhood for the Whanganui River (New Zealand)

The Whanganui River originates in the Tongariro Forest Park, South West of Lake Taupo in New Zealand's North Island, and enters the sea approximately 290 kilometres from the source on the southern coast of the city of Whanganui, entering the Cook Straight. This river holds a sacred value to the indigenous Whanganui Iwi, who consider themselves part of the river – '*Ko au te awa, Ko te awa ko au* – I am the river and the river is me' (Hsiao, 2012: 371).

The legal dispute between the Whanganui Iwi and the government over the river represents the longest-standing legal battle in New Zealand's history and can be traced back more than 100 years. However, two significant developments occurred through the Whanganui River Deed of Settlement in 2011 (a Record of Understanding) and 2012 (Tūtohu Whakatupua) – the salient point in both cases being the 'recognition of the Whanganui River as *Te Awa Tupua* – a living being and entity in its own right' (Hsiao, 2012: 373).

In 2017, this was taken further, and the New Zealand government passed the *Te Awa Tupua* (Whanganui River Claims Settlement) Act (Rowe, 2019: 608). Through this act, the river is considered to hold legal personhood, and the Crown is responsible for maintaining the river in order to 'support the health and well-being' of the river, which includes monetary investment in its management guaranteed for the next 20 years (Rowe, 2019: 609).

Hsiao (2012) highlights the significance of legal personhood for the Whanganui River to earth jurisprudence due to the fundamental principles involved in characterising the river through the law. According to Hsiao (2012: 373), the Whanganui River has been recognised 'as an entity in and of itself – complete . . . as an indivisible and living whole, from the mountains to the sea, incorporating its tributaries and all its physical and metaphysical elements.' As such, this directly mirrors the earth jurisprudence proposed by Berry (2011: 229), who stated that 'every component of the earth community has three rights: the right to be, the right to habitat, and the right to fulfil its role.' Therefore, because the Whanganui River has been granted legal personhood, the river now has the right to be (free from environmental harm – at least in a legal context) and the right to habitat and exist, and the Whanganui Iwi now have a legal recognition of the cultural significance of the river to their being and existence.

The rights of *Pacha Mama* (Ecuador)

In 2008, Ecuador successfully codified the rights of Mother Earth (*Pacha Mama*) into its constitution, representing a milestone for both earth jurisprudence as a philosophy and the development of environmental constitutionalism (heavily debated within environmental ethics). As a result, Article 71 of the Ecuadorian Constitution (Rühs and Jones, 2016: 82, emphasis in original) now states that: *'Nature or "Pachamama," where life is reproduced and exists, has the right to exist, persist, maintain and regenerate its vital cycles, structure, functions and evolutionary processes.'*

Ecuador is an interesting case study for two reasons. Firstly, the pressures to develop the rights of *Pacha Mama* were pushed by a social movement including activists, academics, and non-governmental organisations, but the constitution was approved via a referendum (Espinosa, 2019: 609). This means that there was widespread support for the recognition of rights for nature from a majority of Ecuadorians.

Secondly, the benefit of ensuring Pachamama-like rights into a Constitution rather than legislation is that it is much more difficult to overrule (requiring in most cases a referendum, rather than a simple legislative change). This overcomes some of the aforementioned problems concerning the ToP and state–corporate relationships, because the power to change the Constitution is invested democratically in the people (rather than autocratically). Utilising this rule of law approach whereby *Lex Rex* – law is king (Rühs and Jones, 2016: 179) ensures earth jurisprudence is more fully embedded within human legal systems.

This case study is incredibly important to earth jurisprudence. As Cullinan (2011a: 21) denotes, 'Ecuador changed the debate from whether or not it was possible to recognise rights for nature to whether or not doing so would be effective.'

The rights of nature in Bolivian legislation

Whilst the Bolivian constitution also appreciates the importance of protecting nature, it does not go so far as enshrining the rights of Mother Earth (as in Ecuador). However, such rights are expressed through two Bolivia statutes (Calzadilla and Kotzé, 2018: 399). The first is the Law of the Rights of Mother Earth (LRME), established in 2010, and the second is the Framework Law on Mother Earth and Integral Development for Living Well (enacted in 2012).

The LRME arose out of the 2008 constitutional change recognising the importance of protecting nature and was essentially a precursor to the more extensive Framework Law, which acknowledged the importance of 'living in harmony and balance' with nature (in Article 5; see: Weyer, 2019: 130). Article 7 also detailed 'several specific rights of mother earth,' including the rights to life; to diversity of life; to water; to clean air; to equilibrium; to restoration; and to pollution-free living (Calzadilla and Kotzé, 2018: 410).

Whilst Bolivia represents the very first entrenchment of the rights of nature in domestic-level legislation, Calzadilla and Kotzé (2018: 407) explain how the legislation was a 'watered-down' version of the much more extensive Unity Pact Draft Law (drawn up in correspondence with indigenous organisations), which still maintains a degree of economic development (Weyer, 2019). As a result, this example can be seen as a failure of earth jurisprudential principles to be fully incorporated into the Bolivian legal system in practice. It has been argued that such a shortcoming represents the difficulties in 'counter(ing) deeply vested corporate-driven neoliberal and political economic interests' (Calzadilla and Kotzé, 2018: 400).

The LRME and Framework Law are 'concrete examples in which the law attempts to turn away (if not always successfully) from anthropocentric hierarchies' (Calzadilla and Kotzé, 2018: 423) and towards a more earth-centred jurisprudence.

The three case studies drawn upon here represent some of the major successes of earth jurisprudence and demonstrate the potential of enshrining principles of earth jurisprudence into human-made law. However, they are not the only success stories, as legal personhood has been achieved for the Ganges and Yamuna rivers of the Uttarakhand state (India) in 2017 (O'Donnell, 2018), and 'since 2006, rights of nature have been recognised by some sub-federal public bodies in the United States' (Humphreys, 2017: 459).

However, this chapter (and this particular section) have identified further difficulties in the practicalities of enabling earth jurisprudence. Therefore, more discussion needs to take place in order to address such limitations and how to overcome the (currently) entrenched state–corporate relationships that have such a monumental impact on the development of human laws. As Calzadilla and Kotzé (2018: 423) note, we have to understand that 'law has limitations, and one must remain realistic about its potential to counter deeply vested political, social and economic interests.'

3.6. Conclusion

Bell (2003: 77) once described 'the search for an earth jurisprudence' as 'very much like setting out on a journey in unfamiliar territory without a map.' Therefore, whilst earth jurisprudence as a discipline has a long way to go before it is regularly discussed in tandem with the study of law more broadly, this chapter has highlighted some of the excellent scholarship that has been produced on wild law and earth jurisprudence to date.

Furthermore, this chapter has discussed some of the quintessential historical and theoretical foundations of earth jurisprudence. Particular attention was drawn to the five key principles laid down by Cullinan (2011a: 12) and Koons's (2009, 2011) three seminal guiding principles for earth jurisprudence: the intrinsic value of the earth (subjectivity); the relational responsibility of humanity toward earth (communion); and the democratic governance of the earth community (differentiation) – an extension of the founding text on earth jurisprudence, *The Great Work* (Berry, 1999).

This chapter has also highlighted the similarities and differences between earth jurisprudence and green criminology, laying the foundations for deeper discussions surrounding the integration of the two disciplines in the next chapter. Three case studies were also provided, highlighting real-life success stories of earth jurisprudence in practice. This was achieved by discussing the legal personhood attributed to New Zealand's Whanganui River in 2012, the rights of *Pacha Mama* enshrined into the Ecuadorian Constitution in 2008, and the rights of nature implemented within two Bolivian statutes in 2010 and 2012.

There has also been considerable discussion of some of the current shortcomings of the philosophy of earth jurisprudence. Table 3.2 presented six of the main criticisms of the philosophy. Therefore, this chapter has been realistic in the analysis of earth jurisprudence, which is essential when attempting to understand it in detail. However, despite such criticism, it is clear that the emergences of both green criminology and earth jurisprudence share a central ideology – that current human governance and legal systems are failing to adequately prevent, restrict and make reparations for the sustained environmental harms and degradations that plague the earth in the twenty-first century (issues highlighted in detail in Chapter 1). Therefore, whilst earth jurisprudence may not be a perfect and well-refined philosophy in its present semblance, it is clear that 'without such a jurisprudential shift, Earth and humanity remain at peril' (Koons, 2011: 45).

4 Uniting green criminology and earth jurisprudence

> Green issues open up a wide range of possibilities for interdisciplinary work, both within the social sciences and with disciplines in the natural sciences offering the potential for collaboration between criminologists and economists, geographers, biologists, health specialists, human rights workers, lawyers and others.
>
> (South, 1998: 226, in: Brisman and South, 2020b: 38)

4.1. Introduction

Up until this point, green criminology and earth jurisprudence have been discussed separately, excluding Section 3.4. of Chapter 3, which considered the similarities and differences between the two disciplines. This chapter will begin by highlighting the key objectives and areas of study for both green criminology and earth jurisprudence in order to identify the commonalities between the two (Section 4.2.). This is important, because it will lay the foundation for the central argument of this chapter, which makes a case as to why they should both come together. This will be done by highlighting the fact that both green criminology and earth jurisprudence scholars are working from the *same page*, with the same interests and objectives. The chief purpose of both disciplines, after all, is to identify and address the current state of human actions that contribute to the creation of environmental harms. This is exemplified by leading scholars from each field in the subsequent two quotes: Lynch and Stretesky (2003: 231): 'The purpose of a revitalized green criminology, then, is to redirect attention toward serious and widespread environmental harms that, even more than ordinary crimes, threaten human life and community'; and Murray (2015: 109): 'Drawing upon the altered and more intimate relation to nature and Earth, the overall aim of Earth Jurisprudence is to re-think our understanding of law and governance in a manner that will benefit the whole Earth community.'

Section 4.3. will move on to explain the need for green criminology to generate solutions to environmental problems rather than simply identifying what environmental harms are taking place. The main premise will be that green criminology so far has really only offered three holistic solutions to environmental harms (ToP theory, ecocide, and ecophilosophy), and the discipline (generally) prefers to offer situation-specific, tailor-made solutions to environmental harms. It is therefore suggested that the philosophy of earth jurisprudence contributes a fourth holistic solution to anthropocentrically generated environmental harms, by embedding earth-centred values into human-made laws.

This chapter will finish by discussing the advantages, for both disciplines, in collaborating on research and engaging in theoretical discussions into environmental problems (Section 4.4.).

4.2. Shared objectives and areas of study for green criminology and earth jurisprudence

As outlined in Chapter 2, green criminology is best described and visualised as a perspective (South, 1998) – a medium through which scholars can come together to discuss ideas and conduct research on environmental problems and theories. As a result, green criminology does not specifically have any aims *per se*, other than offering a conceptual framework from which to operate. However, green criminology clearly does have objectives. These are to:

1 Identify anthropocentric environmental harms and crimes of a local and global nature.
2 Explain – through research and theoretical contributions – why environmental harms take place.
3 Offer solutions to the harms identified.
4 By engaging in the first three objectives, environmental harm can be *prevented*, which has benefits for humans, non-humans, and the broader ecologies of the earth.

Similarly, Chapter 3 explored the emerging discipline of earth jurisprudence and specifically analysed the work of Cullinan (2011a), Koons (2008, 2009, 2011, 2012), and Schillmoller and Pelizzon (2013; amongst others). By doing so, there was a realisation that earth jurisprudence is not one specific theory but can be considered a philosophy that may have a number of approaches and interpretations. These include how humans as a species are viewed as one part of the whole earth community and the basic foundations (Koons, 2009, 2011) and underlying principles (Cullinan, 2011a) of an earth jurisprudence. As a result, earth jurisprudence could also – mirroring green criminology – be described as a perspective with several varying meanings to different people. Despite this, earth jurisprudence also has objectives, such as:

1. To recognise that the current mode of human-made law fails to prevent environmental harms from occurring.
2. As a result, the 'correct' way to view law is in line with natural law, the laws of the earth and of the universe. Law is something that already exists, and humans need to realise and accept this law.
3. Principles of earth jurisprudence should be incorporated into wild laws to address environmental harms.
4. Doing so will *prevent* environmental harms from occurring in the first place.

Green criminology and earth jurisprudence are different in the fact that they approach environmental harms in a different way. For green criminology, environmental harm can be overcome through identifying its occurrence, explaining why it has transpired, and then offering (usually) tailor-made solutions in order to prevent environmental harms from reoccurring. Earth jurisprudence takes a different approach rooted in human relationships with (and perspectives of) the natural world with the view that altering our legal approaches can result in the prevention of environmental harm. Therefore, whilst the journey may take a different path, both disciplines want to see a reduction in and the prevention of environmental harm on a global scale – addressing the current exploitation and overuse of the natural world. Some may see this as too closely aligned with environmental political ideology. However, is the aim of a criminologist not to find solutions to prevent criminal behaviour (i.e. punishment, rehabilitation, situational-crime prevention)? And do lawyers not represent their clients with the intention of righting a criminal wrong and protecting the victim from future harm?

I propose that the path to this end goal should be shared by green criminology and earth jurisprudence, or at least they should be brought closer together. So far, there are only a small number of legal scholars writing about earth jurisprudence and wild law compared to the multitude of academic criminologists now engaging in debates about environmental harms. Therefore, by sharing the same path, green criminology could help to raise the profile of earth jurisprudence, adding to theoretical scholarship, sharing and disseminating ideas. On the other hand, earth jurisprudence offers a holistic solution to environmental harms that is virtually untouched within green criminological debates. As a result, I believe both disciplines have a lot to gain from collaborating on research projects and generally sharing and discussing ideas and information. The rest of this chapter will discuss these themes in more detail.

4.3. Focussing on the solutions to environmental harms: differences between green criminology and earth jurisprudence

As Chapter 3 demonstrated, philosophies of earth jurisprudence are concerned with the solutions to environmental harms and that these are manifested in the way that laws are made – in a human-centred fashion rather than earth-centred. As a result, earth jurisprudence recommends a radical shift in the ways that laws are made. As Rühs and Jones (2016: 2) state: '"Earth Jurisprudence" entails a necessary, complete and radical rethink of "legality" in which an anthropocentric ontology is substituted by a more ecocentric one, whilst abandoning the dominant worldview on nature and social organisation.'

The 'solutions' that are proposed through earth jurisprudence can take different forms, representative of different scholars' approaches to earth jurisprudence. However, there is a common appreciation that re-aligning law to recognise the significance of natural earth systems should be the focus and objective of earth jurisprudence. This section is concerned with solutions, so it is worth here providing some examples as to the solutions that some earth jurisprudence scholars have proposed:

1. Wild laws should be constructed with earth systems at the *forefront* (rather than humans). As Koons (2011: 46) denotes, 'a threshold step would be to conceive of Earth at the centre of law and governance, shifting away from purely human-focused systems and appreciating the role of humankind as a part of the broader community of being.'
2. There exists a natural set of laws whereby the earth exists, functions, and reproduces in accordance with such laws. As a result, *human-made law should mirror the laws of nature* rather than solely fulfilling the wants and needs of humans. Cullinan (2010: 2) promotes this way of thinking when he writes: 'the Universe is a self-ordering system which has "natural laws" that govern its functioning and which take precedence over human laws.'
3. Indigenous worldviews often recognise and respect the importance of the natural world (Berry, 1999). Therefore, human-made laws *should incorporate* these ancient belief systems. As Maloney and Siemen (2015: 9) suggest, the 'Earth jurisprudence movement acknowledged

the inspiration and guidance that indigenous cultures and indigenous wisdom can provide to industrialized societies and the development of Earth jurisprudence.'

4 Global environmental harms represent a failure of contemporary human societies to effectively regulate their impact on the environment. Therefore, *creating wild laws in accordance with philosophies of earth jurisprudence will result in the prevention of environmental harms*. This is a central premise of earth jurisprudence, as discussed by Wright (2013: 34), the:

> theory of Earth Jurisprudence suggests that the core failure of modern human governance systems is that they regulate human behavior based on the fallacy that we are separate from nature and can operate outside the boundaries imposed by natural systems.

I have selected these four solutions presented within earth jurisprudence scholarship because they effectively demonstrate the broad, holistic nature of solutions to environmental problems. Whilst green criminology also provides a number of similarly broad explanations and solutions (see explorations of ecophilosophy, ecocide and ToP in Chapter 2), it is arguably more concerned with providing situation-specific solutions to environmental harms and crimes (or simply identifying harms without proposing any answers). I will draw upon three examples here to demonstrate my point.

Greife and Stretesky (2013: 150–166) conducted research examining 'the variation in civil and criminal liability for oil discharges . . . within the United States,' assessing the types of penalties, the minimum and maximum fines attributed to oil discharges, and whether there exists strict liability. The results are not especially important to my argument, but Greife and Stretesky (2013) did find considerable variation in how state law deals with oil discharges. This enabled the authors to make an original contribution to green criminology through presenting their data but also theoretically through connecting their argument with the ToP theory. However, in terms of solutions, Greife and Stretesky (2013: 165) propose 'proper' law enforcement and developing the law. As they state:

> We find space for hope, however, with regard to the development of law. Specifically, concentrated political resistance does appear to influence state oil discharge laws, making those laws easier to enforce and stricter across states . . . in the case of our study, oil discharge laws are important only to the extent that they are used to punish violators and potentially deter would-be violators. Thus, without proper enforcement, laws on the books are meaningless.

Therefore, two things are proposed in this extract. That resistance to environmental offending can act as a solution to environmental harms in terms of deterring offenders, which also makes the laws easier to enforce (presumably because law enforcement agencies have higher justification through public support as opposed to states where resistance is weaker). Secondly, laws can act as a punishment for offenders (in terms of a penalty – monetary or otherwise), and law enforcement can help act as a deterrent. It is undeniable that such solutions might have some short-term effect on environmental offending. Furthermore, this excellent analysis identifies a situation that otherwise would not have been realised. However, my argument is that if a radical shift in the production of law (to an earth-centred perspective) were to take place (at National and State level), then the law on oil discharges would be unanimous across all states, reflecting earth-centred philosophies.

The second example I will use to discuss how green criminology approaches the study of environmental crimes considers fieldwork conducted by Van Uhm and Siegel (2016: 67–87) concerning the illegal trade in black caviar. Drawing upon interviews with informants (people involved in the illegal trade of caviar, such as poachers, smugglers, and 'other informants' – scientists, lawyers, and officials) Van Uhm and Siegel (2016) describe in great detail the extraction of and trafficking in, illegal caviar. Whilst such a study undoubtedly goes a long way in terms of advancing our understanding and knowledge of such illegal trades, there are no solutions offered within the article as to how to overcome the illegal trade in caviar. Such a phenomenon is accepted as 'the way things are.' My argument is that green criminology (much like orthodox criminology) should be solutions focussed. There should be a shared objective that is to address, prevent, and reduce environmental harms. Earth jurisprudence can provide a holistic solution to such harms.

The third and final example of green criminology's approach to providing solutions to environmental harms comes from Rob White (2008a: 179–255, 2008b) – a leading scholar in green criminology – who considers responses to environmental crimes in great detail, particularly considering law, enforcement, regulation, and crime-prevention techniques (it must be noted that this is a common approach to environmental offending from the perspective of green criminologists). White's suggestions for crime prevention strategies follow the traditional green criminological sequence of identifying a harm that has already occurred and suggesting solutions for overcoming the problem in the future. For example, White (2008a: 233) suggests that 'as the threats associated with global warming make clear, there is urgent need for extensive, rigorous and global regulatory systems, systems with teeth.' Therefore, for White (2008a), the solutions to environmental harms can be found in the human-made laws and regulations that attempt to limit (and prevent) environmental harms of the future. As he goes on to note, 'the best way to respond to environmental crime is to prevent it before it occurs' (White, 2008a: 234).

The problem with current environmental crime-prevention strategies (such as those provided by White, 2008b, or Nurse, 2015) is that they are based within contemporary human-made law. Whilst this may seem obvious, addressing environmental harm in this way faces two monumental problems. The first is that human-made laws are designed and implemented through a series of political–economic relationships that place human (and often, corporate) wants and needs at the forefront of lawmaking. The second problem is that it is very clear (partly due to the first problem) that human-made law is current failing, on a devastating scale, to prevent environmental harms (as identified in Chapter 1). Therefore, just as many criminologists have proclaimed that prison does not work as a solution for eliminating recidivism (Bales and Piquero, 2012), or rehabilitating offenders (Bullock and Bunce, 2020), so too it could be claimed that modern legal systems do not work in preventing environmental harm. As Koons (2008: 75) identifies:

> A wholesale moral realignment is necessary because the major human institutions, including law and commerce, have failed their basic purpose. Premised on a discontinuity between humanity and Earth, our chief institutions have denoted value only in the human species. . . . We are witnessing the devastating consequences on Earth of human-centered law, economics, and morality.

The environmental problems identified in Chapter 1 demonstrate the complexity, multiplicity, and deeply entrenched nature of environmental harm within modern society. As a result of these issues, I suggest that green criminology needs to move beyond orthodox ways of providing 'solutions' to environmental crimes. Namely, regulatory and legislative ideals that are largely ineffective in preventing environmental harms. Instead, green criminology needs to expand its theoretical gaze to include philosophies of law that accept and promote a different legal and criminal justice system. A system that focusses on the needs of the whole earth community.

Some will undoubtedly consider that philosophies of earth jurisprudence are beyond the scope of green criminology and should instead be left to the disciplines of law and philosophy. However, my response to this is that green criminology should (and must) have some purpose. It cannot be enough for green criminologists to simply study, examine, and describe environmental problems. It is also naïve to continually blame a lack of robust human-made laws as being guilty of producing such harms. Green criminology can do more than this, can go further than this, and can critically examine (and propose solutions to) human-made laws. Earth jurisprudence is one such solution. It is not a perfect solution. Nor is it a solution ready (or able) to be implemented on a global scale. However, it is a solution that moves beyond simply blaming weak or lax human-made laws that are clearly developed with ulterior motives.

It is worth reiterating here a point I made in Chapter 3. As Bell (2003) suggested, the transition of human-made laws into wild laws embedded within earth jurisprudence is a long and slow one. Therefore, it is important during this transition that green criminology continues to both identify and explain environmental harms, as well as to provide solutions. Such solutions may manifest themselves in traditional crime approaches. For example, global positioning systems (GPS; synonymous with situational-crime prevention approaches, or the electronic tagging of offenders within traditional criminology) have been successfully implemented in remote areas to track endangered animals to prevent them from being poached for meat, ivory, or sport (Banzi, 2014; O'Donoghue and Rutz, 2016). Whilst such responses could have a beneficial effect, they are (ultimately) reactive, often short term, and may result in the simple displacement of crime from one location or offence to another. Therefore, in the long term, green criminologists must look beyond these short-term 'solutions' to broader, holistic theories regarding the transformation of law. I propose that by uniting with earth jurisprudence scholars, green criminologists can start to provide more long-term solutions to the environmental problems that they identify.

4.4. Uniting green criminology and earth jurisprudence

4.4.1. The benefits of collaboration

The title of this book includes the term 'uniting.' Uniting green criminology and earth jurisprudence. By 'uniting,' I am referring to the disciplines themselves and the benefits of discussing green criminology and earth jurisprudence within the same conversation. However, by 'uniting,' I am also referring to those academics, writers, and interested persons operating and researching issues around environmental harm using the perspective of green criminology or the philosophy of earth jurisprudence. Due to both disciplines sharing the same overarching objectives (i.e. to prevent global environmental harms – as discussed in Section 4.2.), much can be achieved by sharing skillsets, information, and ideas. Therefore, my call for interdisciplinary collaboration between earth jurisprudence and green criminology is for the benefit of both disciplines, as well as for the health of the planet in terms of addressing environmental harms.

To me, this potential collaboration is a natural one. Both disciplines are concerned with the prevention of environmental harms from a legal viewpoint. They could be said to be working from the *same page*. Brisman and South (2020b: 5, emphasis in original) have already recognised this, suggesting that 'a number of criminologists have adopted a *legal-procedural* approach to their research on environmental issues, focussing on violations of existing environmental laws.' As a result, many green criminologists are critical of governance and legal systems and therefore promote changes to the law (or tighter legislative and regulatory barriers for environmental offenders) as a solution to green crimes. What green criminology has not done, however, is to envision a radically different approach to lawmaking – as provided by the philosophy of earth jurisprudence. Therefore, green criminologists could use earth jurisprudence as a solution to environmental harms which would involve radically altering our view (as humans) of how we create and administer laws (especially in the Western world). This is radically different from common green criminological solutions to environmental harms that are embedded within the current Western legal systems that promote and facilitate environmental harms.

Uniting green criminology and earth jurisprudence – that is, calling for debate and collaboration between the two – is the type of inter-disciplinary connexion that key authors within green criminology are promoting in their work right now. For example, in the new second edition of the *Routledge International Handbook of Green Criminology*, Brisman and South (2020b: 6) suggest that 'green criminology needs to continue its efforts to forge connections that will take forward theory, policy and practice, developing the perspective both within criminology as well as across other disciplines.' Encouraging debate with earth jurisprudence scholars is something that has not yet materialised. This is not intended to be a criticism, but it is probably due to the infancy of green criminology and earth jurisprudence, as both disciplines are finding their academic feet. Furthermore, encouraging debate between green criminology and earth jurisprudence has the potential of moving both disciplines forward theoretically (as discussed in the following Sections 4.4.2. and 4.4.3.), which directly addresses the purposes of fostering such connections, as explained by Brisman and South (2020b: 6). Part of Brisman and South's (2020b: 7) justification for inter-disciplinary collaboration stems from the nature of environmental harms, where there is a 'need for collaborative, cross-boundary solutions' given the 'transboundary nature of environmental problems.'

Whilst the academic literature suggests there are very few, if any, connections drawn between green criminology and earth jurisprudence, there is evidence to suggest some green shoots in this area are beginning to emerge. In January 2019, myself and Tanya Wyatt (self-professed green criminologists) published an article in *Critical Criminology* using the principles of earth jurisprudence as a potential solution for overcoming the environmental harms inherent with unconventional hydraulic fracturing (known colloquially as 'fracking') in the UK.

Furthermore, Michael Lynch, alongside colleagues Michael Long and Paul Stretesky, published a book in late 2019 recognising the importance of Gaia theory, discussing what it can contribute to green criminological discussions. Gaia can be described as another term for 'the earth system,' which, applied to green criminology, enabled Lynch et al. (2019: 128) to, 'lay out a specific theory of green justice consistent with the health of earth's living ecological system.' This theory involves recognising the significance of Gaia to humans and the natural world and therefore privileging it (the earth system) when considering green justice, and that acts that violate Gaia should therefore be considered green crimes. As Lynch et al. (2019: 128) denote:

> we argue that the life-giving force of Gaia ought to be privileged in theoretical explanations of green justice. Privileging Gaia allows a green theory of justice to emerge where the living earth's reproductive requirements and its life-giving forces are center stage when defining green justice. The privileging of Gaia in this way also allows specification of forms of injustice that violate Gaia's system of justice, and which can also be interpreted as green crimes from the perspective of Gaia.

As a result, the concept of Gaia clearly draws parallels with earth jurisprudence, both theories of which recognise the importance of the earth's natural systems. Lynch et al.'s (2019) work on Gaia and green theories of justice is important considering Lynch (1990) is widely regarded as the creator of the term 'green criminology.' His colleagues are also leading scholars with hundreds of publications within green criminology collectively. It is perhaps not surprising that these scholars have chosen to focus upon Gaia, considering the holistic nature of the theory and considering their main area of research – ToP theory – which is also a holistic political economic theory (and a perspective from which they approach green theories of justice). However, Lynch (2014) has previously made reference to Gaia theory prior to 2019, on the website https://greencriminology.org, which could be considered the first time green criminology and principles of earth jurisprudence have overlapped. In his description of Gaia theory, Lynch (2014: 1) suggests that:

> with respect to green criminology, Gaia Theory provides a way of thinking about ecological organization and issues, and provides a scientific

> grounding for theoretical concepts within green criminology. There are a number of potential uses of this theory within green criminology which have yet to be explored.

Lynch did go on to explore these ideas five years later in his co-authored book entitled *Green Theories of Justice* (Lynch et al., 2019). However, their focus on Gaia in Chapter 6 does not connect with earth jurisprudence. Therefore, the connection between green criminology and earth jurisprudence has not been made until the writing of this book (to the best of my knowledge).

The next section (4.4.2.) will move on to discuss the importance of such a connection. What could earth jurisprudence contribute to the better-established field of green criminology? And what can green criminology do to move forward debates within earth jurisprudence?

4.4.2. What earth jurisprudence can do for green criminology

One of the limitations that I have proposed throughout this book is that green criminology is too engrossed with individualistic solutions to environmental harms and crimes. This may be the result of the formation of a *green* criminology out of the parent discipline of *criminology*, which is exceptionally focussed on human behaviour, deviancy, delinquency, and attempting to understand how and why people engage in behaviours that violate the criminal law. As such, it is possible that earth jurisprudence would view criminology as a discipline that is too focussed on human-made law constructed 'of the people, by the people and for the people' (Koons, 2011: 53), with very little consideration of not just the environment (where environmental laws are concerned) but human conceptions of their relationship with the natural world. It is very hard to conceptualise, for example, how a traditional criminologist writing about penal policy and penal reform would conceive an approach to lawmaking in which humans are not at the centre of concern. As a result, green criminologists – whilst they have made great strides in advancing the criminological gaze to incorporate zemiological thinking in the form of environmental harms as well as crimes – could be criticised as sticking to their criminological roots by offering situation-specific criminological solutions to environmental harms. Therefore, earth jurisprudence has the ability to provide green criminology with a broader, more holistic solution to environmental harms that (whilst it is not perfect and has its limitations – as discussed in Chapter 3), could go some way to addressing such issues *en masse*.

Secondly, earth jurisprudence can offer a unique set of legal skills, knowledge, and experiences to green criminological debates. This is because most scholars writing on earth jurisprudence have a legal background. Cormac Cullinan, for example, is an international environmental lawyer (Cullinan, 2011b). Therefore, green criminology could benefit from the insights of lawyers and the experiences that they bring, particularly with regards to the failing of human-made laws to prevent environmental harms. As Cullinan (2011b: 72) points out, 'it is less obvious to many humans that our governance systems are also failing us.'

Such legal knowledge and perspective would enhance green criminological scholarship, as most criminologists (perhaps unsurprisingly) herald an academic background in criminology. My first degree, for instance was in criminology, and this is where I first encountered the significance of environmental harms and crimes. However, this is only a rule of thumb. Many green criminologists also have a legal background, such as Matthew Hall – a professor of law and criminal justice at the University of Lincoln, UK. The point, however, is that green criminology would benefit from the additional knowledge and experience provided by those earth jurisprudence scholars who have amassed a legal background and vice versa.

Finally, in terms of what earth jurisprudence can contribute to the green criminological arena, earth jurisprudence is primarily concerned with viewing law from a completely different perspective (or set of perspectives) to the common-law view that law is made for (and by) humans. Part of this is that there already exist 'natural laws' – the laws of the universe such as gravity, relativity, and evolution (for example). Earth jurisprudence suggests that this is the 'real' law that will eventually result in humans and the natural world operating in tandem (when and if it is finally implemented by humans). Currently, green criminology (often) attempts to find solutions that are manifested in human-made law, suggesting that such laws can be used as a mechanism to prevent environmental harm. Whilst this is undeniably true in many instances, the complex and varied nature of mass environmental harms means that human-made laws cannot prevent all environmental crimes. After all, we have millions of human-made laws, and yet there still exists mass environmental degradation. Therefore, by assessing the benefits of earth jurisprudence (and considering the natural laws of the universe), green criminology has a lot to gain theoretically.

4.4.3. What green criminology can do for earth jurisprudence

Despite the clear advantages that earth jurisprudence has for green criminology, it is not a one-way street. Green criminology also has a lot to offer earth jurisprudence, and this demonstrates the benefits of inter-disciplinary collaboration.

I propose that earth jurisprudence scholars will be very interested in the work of green criminologists who are also attempting to prevent environmental harms from occurring. In this way, both disciplines can be seen to be operating from the *same page*. Due to the fact that green criminology is at a much more advanced stage (in terms of the number of academic publications), green criminology can help to advance earth jurisprudence by adding to its scholarship, discussing and debating earth jurisprudential concepts, and therefore adding to the scope and breadth of work, increasing the readership to more and more people. This can only be a good thing for earth jurisprudence and for green criminology.

Furthermore, due to the fact that green criminology is much more established, there is a greater volume of theoretical work explaining why there are sustained environmental harms occurring in the 21st century. Such work includes ecophilosophy (Halsey and White, 1998), ToP theory (Stretesky et al., 2014), and ecocide (South, 2014), to name a few examples. Earth jurisprudence can be criticised as focussing too heavily on what earth jurisprudence *is* (which is understandable at such an early stage), without really theorising or providing evidence as to why environmental harm is occurring so prolifically. Therefore, green criminology can go some way to helping earth jurisprudence overcome these conceptual hurdles.

Relatedly, by discussing earth jurisprudential concepts, green criminologists will help to raise the profile of earth jurisprudence outside of the legal discipline, opening up earth jurisprudence to criminologists and other related areas (economics, geography, geology, and the natural sciences). This will help to give earth jurisprudence wider recognition (especially considering the successes of green criminology in recent years). Therefore, green criminology could prevent earth jurisprudence from becoming 'trapped in a realm of ideas' (Schillmoller and Pelizzon, 2013: 14) and stuck within its own discipline without (reaping the benefits of) wider interdisciplinary engagement.

Chapter 3 highlighted three case studies that demonstrated (to some degree) the implementation of earth jurisprudential principles in practice (the legal personhood attributed to the Whanganui River in New Zealand, the Rights of *Pacha Mama* in the Ecuadorian Constitution, and two Bolivian legislations). These are certainly only 'green shoots' for earth jurisprudence, which – whilst significant – only demonstrate that it is possible for humans to recognise earth jurisprudence within human-constructed law. Such examples are few and far between, and the vast majority of the world does not recognise the rights of nature or other concepts within the philosophy of earth jurisprudence. Therefore, earth jurisprudence could be seen to jump too far ahead, proposing the solution to anthropocentrically

Table 4.1 The Benefits of Uniting Green Criminology and Earth Jurisprudence

What earth jurisprudence can do for green criminology	1	Earth jurisprudence presents green criminology with a comprehensive holistic solution to environmental harms that is manifested in a transition from human-centred to earth-centred lawmaking.
	2	Due to the nature of the area of study, most earth jurisprudence scholars have acquired a legal background. By collaborating with green criminologists (many of whom showcase a criminological background), earth jurisprudence (as a discipline) can bring legal knowledge, skills, and ideas to green criminological debates.
	3	By (often) offering situation-specific solutions to environmental harms and crimes, green criminology could be seen to be failing in preventing environmental harm (ultimately, such harms have been exacerbated since the inception of green criminology in the 1990s). Therefore, by offering a radically different legal approach, earth jurisprudence offers green criminology a solution that could intensify the justification behind the need for change, considering the widespread environmental harms that green criminology has identified.
What green criminology can do for earth jurisprudence	1	Green criminology is comparably at a more advanced stage than earth jurisprudence, demonstrated in the number of academic publications in the green criminology discipline (and the greater number of criminologists discussing green issues compared to lawyers writing about earth jurisprudence). Therefore, by engaging with earth jurisprudence, green criminology can advance earth jurisprudence by adding to its scholarship. By discussing and debating earth-centred concepts, green criminology can add to the scope and breadth of work of earth jurisprudence, increasing the reach to a greater quantity of people.
	2	Earth jurisprudence could be seen to focus too heavily on what earth jurisprudence *is* rather than *why* it is so important within contemporary society. Green criminology has been very successful in identifying environmental harms and crimes and therefore can justify the significance of – and need for – an earth jurisprudence.
	3	Green criminology could help to raise the profile of earth jurisprudence by expanding its reach to more diverse areas, preventing earth jurisprudence from becoming 'trapped in a realm of ideas' (Schillmoller and Pelizzon, 2013: 14).
	4	The journey that earth jurisprudence proposes – from human-centred to earth-centred lawmaking – is a long one. Green criminology can offer earth jurisprudence a platform for continually justifying the necessity of earth jurisprudence through the identification of harms that are provided by green criminologists.

induced environmental harms, with little acknowledgement of the long and – perhaps impossible – road from human-made laws constructed for humans to human-made laws that are mutually beneficial for the entire earth community and earth systems. Therefore, green criminology could help earth jurisprudence during this long journey. Green criminology accepts that environmental harms occur on a mass scale, identifies them, and attempts to explain (and then offer solutions) for preventing such harm in the future. As a result, green criminology can be seen to go further than earth jurisprudence in analysing and critiquing environmental harms and crimes. Therefore, earth jurisprudence scholars could use and contribute to the work of green criminologists and strengthen green criminology's theoretical contribution to overcoming environmental harms, suggesting that a solution to eco-problems is rooted in the way that humans make law. Green criminology, then, offers earth jurisprudence a platform for demonstrating the necessity of earth-centred lawmaking by applying its principles to green criminological problems.

In order to sum up the importance of collaboration, Table 4.1 demonstrates the central ideas this chapter has presented in terms of what earth jurisprudence can do for green criminology (and vice versa).

4.5. Conclusion

This chapter has identified why uniting green criminology and earth jurisprudence is a positive and mutually beneficial endeavour for both disciplines. Section 4.2. began by identifying shared objectives and areas of study, providing a platform for further discussion of the similarities and differences between green criminology and earth jurisprudence. The dissimilar approach to the solutions for environmental harms was identified in Section 4.3., suggesting that green criminology often provides reactive, short-term solutions, whereas earth jurisprudence provides a more holistic, long-term approach. The benefits of collaboration were clearly laid out in Section 4.4., which included a summary in Table 4.1. As a result, this chapter has set out the case for why green criminologists and earth jurisprudence scholars should begin dialogue and communication. I am by no means suggesting that doing so will result in the eradication of environmentally harmful acts and practices. However, there are clearly theoretical and practical benefits for both disciplines in working together to identify, examine, explain, and provide solutions to environmental harms and crimes.

The next chapter will identify earth jurisprudential success stories showcasing that the philosophies of earth jurisprudence can work in practice. The intention of doing this is twofold. Firstly, it will overcome (to a minor extent) some of the criticism of earth jurisprudence – that the practicalities of earth-centred legal approaches are impossible to implement in reality (Schillmoller and Pelizzon, 2013). Secondly, analysing the successes of earth jurisprudence will show green criminologists that earth jurisprudence is a legitimate solution to overcoming instances of environmental degradation.

5 Earth jurisprudence in practice

Success stories

> We must remember what ruthless and utter destruction our own species has wrought, not only upon animals, such as the vanished bison and the dodo, but upon its inferior races. The Tasmanians, in spite of their human likeness, were entirely swept out of existence in a war of extermination waged by European immigrants, in the space of fifty years.
>
> (The words of H.G. Wells in *The War of the Worlds*, first published in 1898)

5.1. Introduction

There have already been a number of case studies of environmental harm and wild law presented in this book so far. Chapter 1, for example, discussed mass deforestation, plastic pollution, and ocean gyres, the extinction of non-human animal species, and the production and consumption of animal meat to satisfy the Western diet. Furthermore, relating specifically to wild law, Chapter 3 briefly considered three practical examples whereby earth jurisprudence has been implemented into human-made law (however minimally). This involved consideration of legal personhood for the Whanganui River in New Zealand, the rights of *Pacha Mama* (or Mother Earth) enshrined into the Ecuadorian constitution, and the rights of nature incorporated into Bolivian legislation. These examples are commonly cited within wild law literature (Cullinan, 2011a: 20–22; Humphreys, 2017; Rühs and Jones, 2016). Whilst these are significant, I want to demonstrate in this chapter that successes have been achieved in other parts of the world, signifying the potential of earth jurisprudence in practice. The aim of doing this is to express the viability and validity of the earth jurisprudence argument to green criminologists. The examples that I have selected are fracking for natural gas in Pittsburgh, Pennsylvania (Section 5.2.); the long-term avoidance of deforestation in Suriname (Section 5.3.); and the protection of culturally significant extra-terrestrial heritage sites (Section 5.4.).

5.2. The contradiction between unconventional hydraulic fracturing practices and the Pennsylvanian constitution

The term 'unconventional hydraulic fracturing' (hereafter UHF) refers to an energy extraction process that is primarily targeted at shale formations. These vary but essentially exist deep underground at around 3 kilometres in the UK but at much shallower depths in the US. UHF is a relatively new process (developed by the Mitchell Energy company in the US in the 1980s), that evolved out of conventional hydraulic fracturing (CHF) techniques (Prud'homme, 2014). Very simply, CHF involves drilling into the Earth's surface to the point where a shale formation is reached. A combination of water, sand, and chemicals is then injected into the well at a pressure great enough to force the rock to split (or fracture, creating fissures). This enables naturally existing gas to then escape the shale rock and flow into the well. Pressure is required because shale is a high-porosity, low-permeability geologic formation, which means the natural gas that resides within does not easily flow out of the rock (Speight, 2013). Consequently, shale rock needs to be artificially stimulated to enhance its flow rate. UHF also involves horizontal drilling, which enables the same well to be fractured multiple times. Doing this increases the flow rate even further, making UHF more economically attractive than conventional drilling (because more gas can be collected, on average). UHF is also colloquially referred to as 'fracking' or 'hydro-fracking,' typifying quintessential parts of the process (hydraulic fracturing and using water to create pressure). It has also recently been described as an *extreme* form of energy extraction (Short et al., 2015; Short, 2020), which refers to the unconventional nature of both the process and the target formation (shale).

Whilst fracking goes some way to satisfying the natural gas demands of modern society, it has been heavily criticised (in the media and academic circles) as an extraction process laden with environmental and social problems. These vary from place to place depending on the geological characteristics of the target shale formations and their depth, the operator conducting the UHF, and the laws and regulations of the country or state where the fracking is located. However, the following points are intended to give a flavour of the key issues, which have been split into environmental issues and social issues (although the two often overlap):

Environmental issues

1 UHF has led to the contamination of natural water systems with chemicals used in the process and the naturally occurring matter found deep underground. Furthermore, ground and surface waters can become

contaminated through accidental spillages onsite (Burton Jr et al., 2014: 1680) or truck spillages as chemicals and wastewaters are transported from one place to another (Wiseman, 2011: 9).

2 Where well integrity is compromised (as a result of either induced pressure or earthquakes), water aquifers can become contaminated if all the cases of a well fails (Jackson et al., 2014).
3 The wastewaters generated from a fracking site are highly polluted with chemicals and underground elements. These may be either very difficult and expensive to safely treat or impossible to treat (O'Donnell et al., 2018).
4 The intentional flaring or venting of waste gases is environmentally harmful from the perspective of climate change (Fawole et al., 2016) and human health (Saunders et al., 2018).
5 Fracking generates earthquakes (from either the extraction process or re-injecting wastewaters as a disposal technique into a used well) that have the potential to aid well failure (Ellsworth et al., 2015).

Social issues

1 Fracking can create 'boom-bust' cycles in which a community benefits financially from industry development for a short amount of time, which can negatively impact a community, such as through increasing crime rates (Ruddell, 2017) or affecting a person's mental health (Hirsch et al., 2017).
2 There is some evidence to suggest fracking has a negative impact upon property values, particularly in close proximity to extraction sites (Muehlenbachs et al., 2015).
3 The non-renewable nature of fracking has been criticised as hindering contemporary movements away from fossil fuels and toward more renewable and sustainable forms of energy generation (Lampkin, 2016, 2018, 2020a).
4 Fracking sites require intense management over a short period of time, which can impact the everyday lives of local people. This includes a vast quantity of truck movements (Jackson et al., 2014), as well as dust, noise, and light pollution (Grear et al., 2014).

Despite these negative impacts, UHF has expanded all over the globe but remains most prevalent in the United States. Although shale is easier to extract in the US than it is in the UK (because it is found shallower), the sheer volume of thousands of fracking wells has had a profound effect on people and the environment, particularly in fracking-intensive states such as California, Texas, and Pennsylvania.

From a legal perspective, fracking clearly provides a perfect example of an environmentally destructive anthropocentric endeavour that is legalised in many Western countries. The principles of earth jurisprudence could help to shine a different, earth-centred light on the process resulting in its abolition (Lampkin, 2018; Lampkin and Wyatt, 2019). Whilst fracking remains a controversial yet much-used technique in the US, 'in November 2010 the city of Pittsburgh issued an ordinance that banned natural gas drilling and fracking, elevating community rights and the rights of nature over and above those of corporate personhood' (Humphreys, 2015: 7). This was a colossal achievement given the power and enormity of the natural gas industry in the United States and in Pennsylvania in particular.

Section 27 of Article 1 within Pennsylvania's constitutional declaration was amended in 1971. It specifically stated that 'the people have a right to clean air, pure water, and to preservation of the natural scenic, historic and aesthetic values of the environment' (Van Rossum, 2017: 9). Whilst this amendment is clearly anthropocentrically oriented (and therefore only marginally incorporates earth jurisprudential principles), it served as a critical factor in the Supreme Court of Pennsylvania's decision in *Robinson Township v Commonwealth* (in 2013) to 'strike down, as unconstitutional, a statute that exempted gas companies from complying with local zoning ordinances' (Rinaldi, 2015: 428). This statute was the 2012 Oil and Gas Act. Due to the hierarchical structure of most neo-liberal legal systems (in terms of, for example, judicial precedent and the binding nature of a judge's decisions on lower ranked courts), section 27 took precedence over the Oil and Gas Act. Where this gets interesting from an earth jurisprudential perspective is the reasoning that the court gave for its interpretation of the constitution, which has been described as follows:

> The court also made clear that our environmental rights are not granted by the Pennsylvania Constitution or any legal document created by people. Rather, they are inherent and indefeasible rights given to us by nature, by virtue of our birth, and thus inalienable. The plurality of the court also emphasized that these environmental rights belonged not just to present generations living on the earth, today, but extended to future generations yet to come, thus ensuring a higher obligation of protection.
>
> (Van Rossum, 2017: 10)

As a result, this example demonstrates that wild laws can be implemented even when the intention of the constitution was arguably anthropocentric as opposed to earth-centred. The principles of earth jurisprudence (specifically indefeasible rights that are inalienable), then, could be seen as something to be interpreted and applied from a holistic viewpoint (as opposed to existing in wild law to be later interpreted and abused for the benefit of humans). The Supreme Court of Pennsylvania example therefore demonstrates that the earth-centred interpretation of wild laws is perhaps the most important part of the law itself. However, it is undeniable that a combination of both earth-centred lawmaking and earth-centred interpretation of that law by humans is the most successful way that earth jurisprudence can have a positive environmental benefit.

This is just one example of how earth jurisprudential principles have manifested in human-made laws. However (as Chapter 3 identified), there are several facets to earth jurisprudence. One such feature relates to indigenous worldviews that often encompass higher cultural, spiritual, and religious meanings to the natural world, resulting in a greater degree of respect and a (considerably) lesser degree of ecological destruction. The next section (5.3.) will draw upon an indigenous perspective held within the native forestry communities of southern Suriname, South America. The point is to demonstrate how such worldviews result in greater environmental preservation, showing that the incorporation of such standpoints encapsulates the meaning of earth jurisprudence. As a result, the incorporation into human-made law (if respected) would result in less environmental destruction.

5.3. The forests of Suriname

The Republic of Suriname is a country located in the very north of South America, with the capital, Paramaribo, situated on the northern coastline. Like many countries in Central and South America, Suriname has experienced a troubled history, stemming from European colonisation in the seventeenth century (Zijlstra, 2014). A former Dutch colony, Suriname has a population of only c.500,000, most of whom live in Paramaribo and the surrounding towns and villages in the country's north. In the south, 'the country's interior is home to several tribes of Amerindians and Maroons, descendants of enslaved Africans that escaped into the forests and created their own autonomous, traditional societies' (Van Andel and Havinga, 2008: 1541).

Despite its colonial heritage, Suriname is one of the most forested countries in the world with '94% of the country still covered with natural tropical rain forest' (Food and Agriculture Organization of the United Nations, 2015: 4), leading Suriname to be characterised as a 'high forest cover low deforestation country' (Zalman et al., 2019: 9). This does not mean that Suriname experiences no deforestation. In fact, significant forestry impacts have resulted from the mining of gold (Ramirez-Gomez, 2011), rice production (Latawiec et al., 2014), and selective logging processes in the country (Zalman et al., 2019). However, deforestation in Suriname is audaciously low considering its location in the Amazon rainforest of South America, an area of old-growth forestry that has experienced severe deforestation in Brazil (Boekhout van Solinge and Kuijpers, 2013), Peru (Chávez Michaelsen et al., 2013), and Ecuador (Tapia-Armijos et al., 2015), amongst other countries.

Therefore, how has Suriname managed largely to avoid mass deforestation in contrast to its neighbours? Can green criminologists and earth jurisprudence scholars learn anything from this in an attempt to prevent environmental degradation in other parts of the world?

Several different elements have resulted in the protection of Suriname's natural forestry. One commonly cited factor is the impact of the Reducing Emissions from Deforestation and Forest Degradation (REDD+) program, whereby richer countries provide payments to developing countries if they can evidence an agreed minimal rate of deforestation (Latawiec et al., 2014; Roopsind et al., 2019; Van Oosterzee et al., 2012). However, despite the fact that this aims to provide a monetary incentive to comply with deforestation reduction initiatives, there are many problems with trying to financialise nature conservation in this way. For example, Collins (2019: 38) argues that the REDD+ programme in Suriname and Guyana represents a racialised process that 'contributes to state territorialisation . . . and increases the legibility of forests and their amenability to state management.' Furthermore, there are many issues concerning land use, land ownership, and land accessibility in Suriname, meaning that a lack of rigorous legislation may result in new threats and the exploitation of forestry areas in the future as the demand for Suriname's land and natural resources increases.

Despite the potential of REDD+ to contribute to reductions in carbon emissions and deforestation in Suriname (Roopsind et al., 2019), the cultural and sacred importance of nature to the indigenous inhabitants of forest communities is a further important factor in ecological preservation in this area. Therefore, this relationship between humans and nature – and the resulting environmental preservation that has occurred in Suriname – reflects many themes within the philosophy of earth jurisprudence (such as wholeness, a respect for nature, and humans being one part of that whole). As a result, it is worth considering the value of Suriname's forests to its native inhabitants in more detail.

One of the belief systems in Suriname is the Afro-Christian Winti religion, which – although at times, attempts have been made to repress it – is now an accepted religion of Suriname that can be traced back to the colonial struggles of Caribbean slaves seeking freedom in the 17th century (Collins, 2019: 41). Winti is therefore practiced by many indigenous decedents of such slaves, known as the Surinamese Maroons, and is considered to be a 'magical-religious complex' whereby 'magic, witchcraft, and sorcery' are deemed an important way of life (Green, 1978: 251–251). Within the Winti worldview, there is also a strong connection with nature, which is deemed to have mystical properties and forms an important part of the Winti belief system. As Van Andel (2010: 140) denotes, 'In the Winti worldview, many diseases are caused by a disturbed relationship between human beings and (ancestor) spirits. Disturbance of the environment, such as river pollution, excessive hunting or cutting sacred trees can upset the spirits and cause disaster.'

A similar conception is provided by Green (1978: 163, emphasis in original), who links the meaning of the forest for Maroons to supernatural beings who guard the forest's resources:

> A supernatural being similar to the Earth goddess is *Matu Mama*, the forest mother or goddess. Her domain is the forest, and she is the protector of the animals, plants, and ecological balance in the forest. To those who enter the bush with bad intent she sometimes reveals herself as a being totally covered with hair (or as a woman with very long hair) in order to serve them warning. If a warning is not heeded, *Matu Mama* will arrange illnesses or accidents, but she never kills any sort of offender.

As a result, it is clear to see that there is a cultural, spiritual, and religious significance to forestry contained within the views of the Surinamese Maroons. One aspect of earth jurisprudence focuses on the significance of indigenous traditions. Berry (1999), regarded as the founder of earth jurisprudence, advocated the importance of indigenous wisdom to the 'great jurisprudence' because of the 'intimacy with and participation in the functioning of the natural world' (Berry, 1999: 177). For Berry, this way of viewing and respecting nature is pivotal and should be the accepted version of law (as opposed to contemporary, Western-made law influenced by politics, economics, and business; Berry, 1999: 14–15). Therefore, indigenous governance systems that respect natural laws (the laws of mother nature and of the universe, for example) are a central facet to those earth jurisprudence scholars writing about indigenous philosophies of law. As Hosken (2011: 26) suggests, what Berry

> had identified was the legal principle which is universal to all indigenous governance systems. The earth is the primary source of law. Law exists. We are born into a lawful and ordered universe. Humans cannot make law but must be aware of it,

just as many indigenous communities are aware of the natural laws that exist in the universe.

These thoughts within indigenous earth jurisprudence can be seen to partially reflect the Winti worldview of the Surinamese Maroons (as described earlier). However, the indigenous Winti version of natural law is based within the very specific Afro-American Christian beliefs that draw strongly on sorcery and magic rather than specifically the laws of mother nature and the universe. However, the Maroons are not the only forest-dwelling native group inhabiting the Surinamese forests. The Saramacca people also attribute sacred meaning to the forests. As Hoffman (2013: 341) explains:

> The Saramacca have an elaborate land tenure system and traditional spiritual beliefs that result in strict controls over forest and resource use. During this research, old-growth forests in the village vicinity were off-limits to locals and researchers for two or more days a week to appease forest and ancestor spirits. Some plant taxa were taboo . . . (and to be) avoided when cutting forest plots. Based upon Saramacca traditions, visiting the forest on a forbidden day, cutting down a taboo plant, or using a forest resource on someone's land without permission could result in untold suffering or death for an entire lineage. . . . It appears that the Saramacca sociocultural system, as currently practiced, affords greater ecological resilience and protection of biodiversity in local forests.

It is clear to see, then, that indigenous beliefs about land use and access have played a significant role in the historical preservation of Surinamese forestry, where a respect for nature has been engrained within indigenous populations for centuries (if not longer). However, there is evidence to suggest that the modern neo-liberal world is catching up with Suriname, which could result in unprecedented deforestation in the country in the near future (Redd+ Suriname, 2020). Gold mining is one such driver of deforestation that is likely to affect Suriname in the coming decades, a theme identified by Dezécache et al. (2018: 3), who suggested that, 'in 2010 around 10% of the national GDP was attributed to goldmining.'

However, the point of exploring the unusual situation of environmental protection in Suriname has been to demonstrate how indigenous beliefs about forestry, Mother Earth, and the universe have resulted in the preservation of the environment rather than the destruction of it – as is the case with the majority of the earth that is dominated by industrial capitalism. Doing this suggests that an approach to lawmaking that respects nature results in ecological preservation. It is arguable that the foundations for such beliefs (magical, cultural, or religious) are largely irrelevant. What is important, however, is the human conception of the relationship between humankind and nature, where both exist in equilibrium (earth jurisprudence), as opposed to the domination of humans over the natural world (neo-liberal societies). Therefore, Suriname can be envisaged as an earth jurisprudential success, albeit one that may be decimated in the coming decades.

A further earth jurisprudence success has been witnessed outside of the confines of planet Earth with regards to the potential development of extra-terrestrial heritage sites.

5.4. Extra-terrestrial objects and cultural heritage sites in outer space

Humankind has long been curious about its place within the universe and what (if anything) exists beyond the confines of planet Earth. The Cold War era, synonymous with the 'space age,' turned wonder into reality. In 1957, the Soviet Union successfully launched the world's first artificial satellite (Sputnik-1) into Earth orbit, closely followed in 1958 by Sputnik-2 and the US Explorer Satellite (Lampkin, 2020b). In 1969, US astronauts walked on the moon during the successful Apollo 11 lunar mission.

Since these first explorations into outer space, humans have gained a great degree of scientific knowledge and understanding. In fact, the space industry has expanded to such a degree that it is now possible to pay as a private party to enter space as a tourist (Denis et al., 2020). Furthermore, four private start-up companies in the US have emerged in recent years interested in lunar (and otherwise extra-terrestrial) mining (Takemura, 2019). Simply put, this is the intentional extraction of minerals and energy resources that exist on celestial bodies outside of planet Earth, such as on moons, asteroids, or other planets. The aim is to explore for materials that can be extracted, transported, and then used on planet Earth. In 2005, Japan's *Hayabusa* spacecraft successfully landed on asteroid 25143 Itokawa and found achondrites (source of platinum-group metals) and chondrites (containing water; Lampkin, 2020b; Yurimoto et al., 2011: 1116), signalling that such a reality might not be too far away.

The military and political tensions between the United States and the Soviet Union during the cold war sparked international attention, as fears about nuclear armament and space warfare were feared as possible prizes for the winners of the space race. Thankfully, this did not materialise, but international concern led to the development of the 1967 Outer Space Treaty (OST) by the United Nations Committee on the Peaceful Use of Outer Space (USCOPUOS), an agreement between signatories regarding the regulation 'use, occupation, and appropriation of space' (Quinn, 2008: 480).

There is no wild law within the OST. Of the 17 articles, only article II has any relevance to arguments about earth jurisprudence. It reads as follows: 'Article II – Outer space, including the moon and other celestial bodies, is not subject to national appropriation by claim of sovereignty, by means of use or occupation, or by any other means' (Garber, 2006).

Article II is important insofar as it prohibits the national appropriation of matter in outer space. There is a recognition, therefore, that the existence of celestial objects is of significance to humans and that such resources should be shared and used communally. However, it is undeniable that the Cold War and global politics were at the forefront of the minds of USCOPUOS when drafting the OST.

The OST is often regarded as the beginning of international collaboration on matters regarding outer space. However, this and many other international law guidelines are non-binding, such as those regarding the ownership of space objects and how to prevent the creation of space debris (Gupta, 2019). Therefore, some nations have been using domestic law in an attempt to protect their interests. One such example is legislation from the United States – The Apollo Lunar Legacy Landing Act (ALLLA) of 2013, which proposed that the original 1969 lunar landing site (and the equipment that still resides there) is a US National Park (Hertzfeld and Pace, 2013). The problem with the ALLLA is section 4 (relating to definitions), which states that 'the Apollo Landing Sites National Historic Park would include "all areas of the Moon where astronauts and instruments . . . touched the lunar surface"' (Ellis, 2015: 547). This clearly contravenes article II of the 1967 OST relating to national appropriation and claims of sovereignty.

Regardless of the legal trepidations regarding ALLLA, there is significance to wild law and earth jurisprudence debates where attempts are made to preserve extra-terrestrial sites from future human interference and destruction. After all, some earth jurisprudence scholars have expanded the scope of the discipline to include the wider universe rather than just planet Earth, linking cosmology and earth jurisprudence (Berry, 1999; Greene, 2011; Loder, 2018). As a result, human attempts to preserve sites such as those of cultural significance on the moon can be interpreted as representing a type of earth jurisprudence, or what Loder (2018: 298) would term 'space jurisprudence.'

Whilst the Apollo 11 lunar landing site is often regarded as culturally significant to humans (representing the first time a human stepped foot on another celestial body), a number of other exo-locations could also be considered in this way, such as the landing site of *Viking-1* on Mars in 1976 (Matthews and McMahon, 2018). Furthermore, Halley's comet (which is only visible from Earth roughly every 76 years) could be recognised as culturally significant to humans, having been observed several times in history. Most notably, Halley appeared in 1066 during the turmoil produced by the death of King Edward of England, 'hailed an omen during the Norman conquest that followed, and its image was famously embroidered in the Bayeux Tapestry' (Matthews and McMahon, 2018: 57).

The desire of nations to protect culturally significant places in the universe could be seen to represent an acknowledgement of earth jurisprudential principles – that such places should be protected from harm or interference in the collective interests of humanity. The site of the 1969 lunar landing, in particular, is important due to it representing the first time humankind stepped foot on another celestial body. In order to protect such historic sites and to prevent the future destruction of extra-terrestrial bodies from extreme-energy mining, space jurisprudence could provide international law with the foundation for such preservation by integrating earth jurisprudential principles (such as the whole community of the universe, inclusive of both humans and non-humans).

In relation to the argument in this book that protecting culturally significant sites in outer space represents a 'success story,' it is acknowledged that this is a fairly radical take on applied earth jurisprudence. The very name itself – *earth* jurisprudence – fails to adequately capture ecological issues pertaining to outer space. Therefore, a *universal jurisprudence* may be a more appropriate lexicon to encompass the entirety of matter that exists in the universe (or multiverse). Loder's (2018) adoption of the term 'space jurisprudence' (the origin of the exact coining of this term is unknown, but it could be traced back to the 1950s and found in the writings of Crane (1963), Haley (1958), and Katzenbach (1958) – as an extension of earth jurisprudence – might be enough to enable further discussions of space heritage within earth jurisprudential debates. What is clear, however, is that the consideration of matter beyond earth is worthy of consideration by earth jurisprudence scholars and green criminologists alike (Lampkin, 2020b; Takemura, 2019). Broader concepts of the universe are deep rooted within earth jurisprudence (Berry, 1999) and demonstrate a kinship with environmental ethics (to take from Koons, 2011: 45).

5.5. Conclusion

The aim of this chapter was to highlight some real-world examples of earth jurisprudence working in practice. This began with Section 5.2., which discussed the significance of the Supreme Court of Pennsylvania's 2013 ruling in the *Robinson Township v Commonwealth* case concerning the natural gas industry's potential exemption from local zoning ordinances (Rinaldi, 2015). Whilst Section 27 of article 1 of the Pennsylvanian constitution clearly had the *human* interests to a healthy environment in mind, it was interpreted by the Supreme Court in a way that represented earth jurisprudential principles. Specifically, this was that such rights exist not because they are awarded in the constitution but because they are given to us by nature (Van Rossum, 2017) and therefore occur naturally. This was a significant development in the lawmaking of a Western nation in which the natural gas industry is powerful, dominant, and exempt from many other environmental laws and regulations, such as the *Clean Air Act*, *Clean Water Act*, and the *Safe Drinking Water Act* (Brady and Crannell, 2012: 43, emphasis added).

Section 5.3. moved on to discuss the indigenous worldviews of native Suriname populations, who attribute a cultural and spiritual significance to the old-growth forests that they inhabit in the southern Surinamese Amazon. Whilst there was no specific analysis of existing law, the point was to demonstrate how respecting and implementing such worldviews into wild laws would lead to a lesser level of environmental destruction (compared to current anthropocentrically focussed laws that facilitate environmental harms). Suriname was drawn upon as an example due to its relative success with regards to preventing deforestation. Ultimately, Suriname still has more than 90% of its old-growth forests intact, making it one of the most forested tropical countries in the world (Werger, 2011: v).

Finally, Section 5.4. sought to add a different dimension to common wild law debates by discussing earth jurisprudential principles related to extraterrestrial matter. This argument was placed in contemporary context and highlighted the recent emergence of harmful practices to the astro environment (such as space tourism, extreme-energy mining, and culturally significant celestial heritage sites such as the Apollo 11 lunar landings in 1969 or the *Viking-1* soft landing on Mars in 1976).

Most arguments within earth jurisprudence focus on the high-profile cases of the Ecuadorian constitution (the Rights of *Pacha Mama*), the legislative successes in Bolivia, and the legal personhood granted to the Whanganui River of New Zealand. Whilst these are undoubtedly significant, I chose to pick lesser-cited examples of earth jurisprudential successes in order to enhance our critical thinking with regards to wild law and demonstrate that the principles of earth jurisprudence can be successful in practice as well as theory. This is pivotal if earth jurisprudence is to refrain from becoming 'trapped in a realm of ideas' (Schillmoller and Pelizzon, 2013: 14).

The next chapter will move on to discuss some concluding thoughts with regards to green criminology and earth jurisprudence, tying together the central arguments presented within this book.

6 Concluding thoughts

> Our biosphere is sick and is behaving like an infected organism. As carbon has been collecting in our atmosphere, it has also been accumulating in the ocean and as time has passed, deforestation, soil erosion, vanishing wetlands and a whole host of other problems have continued unabated. We face a convergence of crises, all of which present a significant moral and survival challenge for the human species.
>
> (Burdon, 2015: 1)

6.1. Introduction

The health and well-being of planet Earth matter to everyone: humans, non-human animals, ecosystems, and future generations of all of these inhabitants. However, the richness of the planet's biodiversity is being degraded at an alarming rate, leading several scholars to suggest that we have now left the Holocene geological epoch and are entering the Anthropocene (Crutzen and Stoermer, 2000; Shearing, 2015; Zalaseiwicz et al., 2010).

Contemporary legal systems are products of societal attempts to manage and regulate human behaviours, describing actions that the majority find either acceptable or unacceptable. This is why we have the academic disciplines of law and criminology: to study the making and administering of laws and regulations (law) and to analyse behaviours that violate those laws (criminology). Legal systems have therefore always been constructed with humans at the centre. They are developed 'of the people, by the people and for the people' (Koons, 2011: 53). As Burdon (2013: 818) denotes: 'reflecting a vast heritage of anthropocentric philosophy and theology, the dominant concept of law in analytic jurisprudence is fundamentally human centred.'

Environmental law is a relatively recent phenomenon, and the volumes of such laws have increased in recent years both as a greater number of environmental problems emerge, and human populations continue to grow and become more complex. Nevertheless, laws are still constructed (on the whole) with humans in mind and the environment (where applicable) on the periphery. This book has suggested that the current way of making law (in a human-centred fashion) and analysing criminal law violations has led to humans over-powering nature. This has resulted in the facilitation, as opposed to the protection, of environmentally harmful practices that degrade the natural world. This is the general rule and there are exceptions to it which have been outlined in Chapters 3 (considering earth jurisprudence) and 5 (proposing earth jurisprudence success stories).

Both green criminologists and earth jurisprudence scholars recognise that the current way of *doing* law and criminology fails to account for the needs of other-than-human parties, such as non-human animals, the climate, biodiversity, and eco-systems. However, these sub-disciplines do not interact or communicate, despite their shared purpose. I have suggested (largely in Chapter 4) that both earth jurisprudence and green criminology stand to benefit greatly from fostering a partnership. These benefits include information sharing, debate, collaboration on primary and theoretical research projects, and learning from each other's legal and criminological knowledge and skills. Applied to the study of environmental harm and degradation, such collaboration could be very powerful indeed.

6.2. A summary of the book

One of the aims of this book was to provide a bridge uniting green criminology and earth jurisprudence. In order to achieve this, the book has taken a very particular path. Chapter 1 began with introducing the reader to issues of global environmental harm. There is no sense in discussing green criminology and earth jurisprudence without a basic understanding of the global environmental issues that give meaning and significance to the two disciplines. As a result, this chapter encompassed a number of examples and case studies of environmental degradation, exemplifying the magnitude of global anthropocentric environmental harms. Such examples included mass deforestation of the Earth's old-growth tropical rainforests, the extinction of the earth's ecology and non-human species, the pollution of the world's oceans with plastics and other hazardous and non-biodegradable matter, and the use, abuse, and consumption of animals to satisfy Western diets. Conceptualising global environmental harm in this way provided a platform for discussing earth jurisprudence and green criminology, and their relationship with researching and theorising about human relationships with the natural world.

Chapters 2 and 3 began by detailing what green criminology and earth jurisprudence mean, how they emerged as academic disciplines, and what the central theoretical frameworks are. This was accompanied by a comprehensive critique of each discipline. Additionally, three case studies were presented in Chapter 3 (regarding Bolivia, Ecuador, and New Zealand) to show that the theoretical basis of earth jurisprudence can be realised in practice. These themes were expanded upon in Chapter 5, which used the examples of Pennsylvania, Suriname, and outer space to offer lesser-cited examples of how principles of earth jurisprudence can succeed in practice.

Chapter 4 is perhaps the most important chapter of this book, as it attempted to construct the theoretical bridge between earth jurisprudence and green criminology. This chapter highlighted the shared motives and objectives of each discipline and what can be achieved for both parties by collaborating on criminological and legal environmental issues. Furthermore, Section 4.3. focussed on the differences between the proposed solutions to environmental harms that differ between green criminology and earth jurisprudence and how green criminology can benefit from the holistic, earth-centred approach to environmental problems.

This chapter seeks to conclude discussions by describing what the book has done so far (Section 6.2.) and what the main points are for the reader to take away (Section 6.3.).

6.3. Key points to take away

Some may think that the proposed unison of green criminology and earth jurisprudence is beyond the purview of both disciplines. However, this book has made a case for discussing both disciplines together. As a result, the key concepts to take away from this analysis are as follows:

1 Both earth jurisprudence and green criminology are relatively new developments within their parent disciplines: law and criminology. They share the same foundations that are based on the premise that legal systems are currently failing to prevent widespread global environmental harms and that such a situation is worthy of academic consideration. Therefore, both disciplines are working from the *same page* and have similar aims and objectives.
2 By working together and collaborating on academic research projects, both green criminology and earth jurisprudence can advance their disciplines through enhanced theoretical contributions. Through information and knowledge exchange, critical debate and pooling skills and resources, both disciplines can create thought-provoking arguments and solutions to environmental harms and crimes.

3 Earth jurisprudence has the ability to contribute significantly to green criminological debates regarding the solutions to anthropocentrically induced environmental problems. This is because earth jurisprudence provides a holistic, earth-centred approach to lawmaking, which it considers as able to (if successfully implemented) contribute to the reduction of environmental degradation. Green criminology has not yet considered this solution, which would be a welcome accompaniment to the few other existing holistic explanations of green crimes (such as ToP theory, ecophilosophy, and ecocide).
4 Conversely, green criminology can offer much to earth jurisprudence. There exists a larger body of academic literature on green crimes (compared to earth jurisprudence scholarship). As a result, green criminologists can help to raise the profile of earth jurisprudence by using its principles to explain environmental harms. This will add to the breadth of work within the earth jurisprudence literature and prevent it from becoming 'trapped in a realm of ideas' (Schillmoller and Pelizzon, 2013: 14).
5 By considering solutions to environmental harms and crimes, both green criminologists and earth jurisprudence scholars are addressing one of the biggest challenges of our generation: how to curb the current domination of humans over the natural world. By doing so, green criminology is extending the theoretical reach of criminology, which traditionally only considers behaviours that constitute the violation of criminal laws. Adjacently, earth jurisprudence is extending the theoretical reach of the legal discipline by accepting the failings associated with human-centred Western legal systems.

These five key points emphasise the importance and suitability of uniting green criminology and earth jurisprudence for the benefit of global ecological health.

6.4. Conclusion

I hope that this book will spark a dialogue between green criminologists and earth lawyers with regards to collaborating on academic work pertaining to environmental harms. A critical approach has been taken to the study of both disciplines to highlight key grounds for theoretical engagement and enhancement. I have provided several real-life examples and case studies of earth jurisprudential principles emerging in practice. However, these realities are few and far between, and the fact remains that our human-centred approach to lawmaking is exacerbating environmental harms rather than protecting the natural world. I do not profess that uniting green criminology and earth jurisprudence is the answer to all of our environmental problems. Nevertheless, if scholars researching in both disciplines can contribute to critical thinking about environmental legal problems, then this may go some way to influencing our approach to drafting and administering laws and regulations. To borrow from the final line of Rob White's (2008a) seminal text *Crimes Against Nature*, 'our lives – and the lives of future generations and ecosystems – depend on it.'

References

Agnew, R. (2013) 'The Ordinary Acts that Contribute to Ecocide: A Criminological Analysis,' in: South, N. and Brisman, A. (eds) *The Routledge International Handbook of Green Criminology*. Abingdon: Routledge.

Alberg, A.J. Shopland, D.R. and Cummings, K.M. (2014) 'The 2014 Surgeon General's Report: Commemorating the 50th Anniversary of the 1964 Report of the Advisory Committee to the US Surgeon General and Updating the Evidence on the Health Consequences of Cigarette Smoking,' *American Journal of Epidemiology*, 179(4): 403–412.

Amos, A. (1996) 'Women and Smoking,' *British Medical Bulletin*, 52(1): 74–89.

Bales, W.D. and Piquero, A.R. (2012) 'Assessing the Impact of Imprisonment on Recidivism,' *Journal of Experimental Criminology*, 8: 71–101.

Banzi, J.F. (2014) 'A Sensor Based Anti-Poaching System in Tanzania National Parks,' *International Journal of Scientific and Research Publications*, 4(4): 105–111.

Batrićević, A. (2018) 'Social, Economic and Political Factors of Environmental Crime,' *Thematic Conference Proceedings of International Significance: Academy of Criminalistics and Police Studies*, 1(13): 137–148.

Beirne, P. (2019) 'Animals, Women and Terms of Abuse: Towards a Cultural Etymology of Con(e)y, Cunny, Cunt and C*nt,' *Critical Criminology*, 2019: 1–23.

Bele, M.Y. Sonwa, D.J. and Tiani, A.M. (2014) 'Adapting the Congo Basin Forests Management to Climate Change: Linkages Among Biodiversity, Forest Loss, and Human Well-Being,' *Forest Policy and Economics*, 50(2014): 1–10.

Bell, M. (2003) 'Thomas Berry and an Earth Jurisprudence,' *The Trumpeter: Journal of Ecosophy*, 19(1): 69–96.

Berry, T. (2011) 'Rights of the Earth: We Needs a New Legal Framework Which Recognises the Rights of All Living Beings,' in: Burdon, P. (ed) *Exploring Wild Law: The Philosophy of Earth Jurisprudence*. Mile End, Australia: Wakefield Press.

Berry, T. (1999) *The Great Work: Our Way Into the Future*. New York: Three Rivers Press.

Bigagli, E. (2016) 'The International Legal Framework for the Management of the Global Oceans Social-Ecological System,' *Marine Policy*, 68: 155–164.

Binkley, D. Campoe, O.C. Alvares, C. Carneiro, R.L. Cegatta, Í. and Stape, J.L. (2017) 'The Interactions of Climate, Spacing and Genetics on Clonal Eucalyptus

Plantations Across Brazil and Uruguay,' *Forest Ecology and Management*, 405: 271–283.

Birnbacher, D. (1998) 'Legal Rights for Natural Objects: A Philosophical Critique,' in: Morsher, E. Neumaier, O. and Simons, P. (eds) *Applied Ethics in a Troubled World*. Boston: Kluwer Academic Publishers.

Boekhout van Solinge, T. (2016) 'Deforestation in the Brazilian Amazon,' in: Shroder, J.F. and Sivanpillai, R. (eds) *Biological and Environmental Hazards, Risks, and Disasters*. Amsterdam: Elsevier.

Boekhout van Solinge, T. and Kuijpers, K. (2013) 'The Amazon Rainforest: A Green Criminological Perspective,' in: South, N. and Brisman, A. (eds) *The Routledge International Handbook of Green Criminology*. Abingdon: Routledge.

Brady, W.J. and Crannell, J.P. (2012) 'Hydraulic Fracturing Regulation in the United States: The Laissez-Faire Approach of the Federal Government and Varying State Regulations,' *Vermont Journal of Environmental Law*, 14: 39–70.

Brisman, A. (2015) 'Multicolored' Green Criminology and Climate Change's Achromatopsia,' *Contemporary Justice Review*, 18(2): 178–196.

Brisman, A. and South, N. (2020a) 'Introduction: New Horizons, Ongoing and Emerging Issues and Relationships in Green Criminology,' in: Brisman, A. and South, N. (eds) *Routledge International Handbook of Green Criminology*. Abingdon: Routledge. 2nd Edition.

Brisman, A. and South, N. (2020b) 'The Growth of a Field: A Short History of "Green" Criminology,' in: Brisman, A. and South, N. (eds) *Routledge International Handbook of Green Criminology*. Abingdon: Routledge. 2nd Edition.

Brisman, A. and South, N. (2016) 'Water, Inequalities and Injustice: Social Divisions, Racism and Colonialism – Past and Present,' *Criminal Justice and Security in Central and Eastern Europe: Safety, Security, and Social Control in Local Communities: Conference Proceedings*, 2016: 359–366.

Brisman, A. South, N. and Walters, R. (2018) 'Climate Apartheid and Environmental Refugees,' in: Carrington, K. Hogg, R. Scott, J. and Sozzo, M. (eds) *The Palgrave Handbook of Criminology and the Global South*. Cham: Palgrave Macmillan.

Bryman, A. (2016) *Social Research Methods*. Oxford: Oxford University Press. 5th Edition.

Bu, M. Lin, C.T. and Zhang, B. (2016) 'Globalization and Climate Change: New Empirical Panel Data Evidence,' *Journal of Economic Surveys*, 30(3): 577–595.

Buell, F. (2003) *From Apocalypse to Way of Life: Environmental Crisis in the American Century*. New York: Routledge.

Bullock, K. and Bunce, A. (2020) '"The Prison Don't Talk to You About Getting Out of Prison": On Why Prisons in England and Wales Fail to Rehabilitate Prisoners,' *Criminology and Criminal Justice*, 20(1): 111–127.

Burdon, P.D. (2015) *Earth Jurisprudence: Private Property and the Environment*. Abingdon: Routledge.

Burdon, P.D. (2013) 'The Earth Community and Ecological Jurisprudence,' *Oñati Socio-Legal Series*, 3(5): 815–837.

Burdon, P.D. (2011a) 'Eco-Centric Paradigm,' in: Burdon, P.D. (ed) *Exploring Wild Law: The Philosophy of Earth Jurisprudence*. Mile End, Australia: Wakefield Press.

Burdon, P.D. (2011b) 'The Great Jurisprudence,' in: Burdon, P.D. (ed) *Exploring Wild Law: The Philosophy of Earth Jurisprudence*. Mile End, Australia: Wakefield Press.

Burdon, P.D. (2010) 'Wild Law: The Philosophy of Earth Jurisprudence,' *Alternative Law Journal*, 35(2): 62–65.

Burton Jr, G.A. Basu, N. Ellis, B.R. Kapo, K.E. Entrekin, S. and Nadelhoffer, K. (2014) 'Hydraulic "Fracking": Are Surface Water Impacts an Ecological Concern?' *Environmental Toxicology and Chemistry*, 33(8): 1679–1689.

Calzadilla, P.V. and Kotzé, L.J. (2018) 'Living in Harmony with Nature? A Critical Appraisal of the Rights of Mother Earth in Bolivia,' *Transnational Environmental Law*, 7(3): 397–424.

Cao, A.N. and Wyatt, T. (2016) 'The Conceptual Compatibility Between Green Criminology and Human Security: A Proposed Interdisciplinary Framework for Examinations into Green Victimisation,' *Critical Criminology*, 24(3): 413–430.

Carić, H. and Mackelworth, P. (2014) 'Cruise Tourism Environmental Impacts – The Perspective from the Adriatic Sea,' *Ocean and Coastal Management*, 102: 350–363.

Ceballos, G. Ehrlich, P.R. and Dirzo, R. (2017) 'Biological Annihilation via the Ongoing Sixth Mass Extinction Signaled by Vertebrate Population Losses and Declines,' *Proceedings of the National Academy of Sciences*, 114(30): E6089–E6096.

Chassin, L. Presson, C.C. Sherman, S.J. and Edwards, D.A. (1990) 'The Natural History of Cigarette Smoking: Predicting Young-Adult Smoking Outcomes from Adolescent Smoking Patterns,' *Health Psychology*, 9(6): 701–716.

Chávez Michaelsen, A. Huamani Briceño, L. Fernandez Menis, R. Bejar Chura, N. Valera Tito, F. Perz, S. Brown, I.F. Domínguez Del Aguila, S. Pinedo Mora, R. and Alarcón Aguirre, G. (2013) 'Regional Deforestation Trends Within Local Realities: Land-Cover Change in Southeastern Peru 1996–2011,' *Land*, 2(2): 131–157.

Cohen, J.E. (2010) 'Population and Climate Change,' *Proceedings of the American Philosophical Society*, 154(2): 158–182.

Collin, R. (1994) 'Review of the Legal Literature on Environmental Racism, Environmental Equity and Environmental Justice,' *Journal of Environmental Law and Litigation*, 9: 121–170.

Collins, Y.A. (2019) 'Colonial Residue: REDD+, Territorialisation and the Racialized Subject in Guyana and Suriname,' *Geoforum*, 106: 38–47.

Crane, R.D. (1963) 'The Beginnings of Marxist Space Jurisprudence?' *American Journal of International Law*, 57(3): 615–625.

Cressey, D.R. (2016) 'The Plastic Ocean,' *Nature*, 536(7616): 263–265.

Cressey, D.R. (1951) 'Criminological Research and the Definition of Crimes,' *American Journal of Sociology*, 56(6): 546–551.

Crutzen, P.J. and Stoermer, E.F. (2000) 'The Anthropocene,' *Global Change Newsletter*, 41: 17–18.

Cullinan, C. (2011a) 'A History of Wild Law,' in: Burdon, P.D. (ed) *Exploring Wild Law: The Philosophy of Earth Jurisprudence*. Mile End, Australia: Wakefield Press.

Cullinan, C. (2011b) *Wild Law: A Manifesto for Earth Justice*. Devon: Green Books. 2nd Edition.

Cullinan, C. (2010) *The Legal Case for the Universal Declaration of the Rights of Mother Earth* [Online]. Available at: https://therightsofnature.org/wp-content/uploads/pdfs/Legal-Case-for-Universal-Declaration-Cormac-Cullinan.pdf (Accessed: 30th April 2020).

Damtie, M. (2011) 'Anthropocentric and Ecocentric Versions of the Ethiopian Legal Regime,' in: Burdon, P.D. (ed) *Exploring Wild Law: The Philosophy of Earth Jurisprudence*. Mile End, Australia: Wakefield Press.

Dauvergne, P. and Lister, J. (2011) *Timber*. Cambridge: Polity Press.

Denis, G. Alary, D. Pasco, X. Pisot, N. Texier, D. and Toulza, S. (2020) 'From New Space to Big Space: How Commercial Space Dream Is Becoming a Reality,' *Acta Astronautica*, 166: 431–443.

Dezécache, C. Salles, J.M. and Hérault, B. (2018) 'Questioning Emissions-Based Approaches for the Definition of REDD+ Deforestation Baselines in High Forest Cover/Low Deforestation Countries,' *Carbon Balance and Management*, 13: 1–12.

Donoso, A. (2017) 'Representing Non-Human Interests,' *Environmental Values*, 26(5): 607–628.

Eckersley, R. (2011) 'Representing Nature,' in: Alonso, S. Keane, J. Merkel, W. and Fotou, M. (eds) *The Future of Representative Democracy*. New York: Cambridge University Press.

Ellis, K. (2015) 'Preserving Apollo: HR 2617 and the Creation of the Apollo Lunar Landing Sites National Historical Park,' *Fordham Environmental Law Review*, 26(3): 516–558.

Ellsworth, W.L. Llenos, A.L. McGarr, A.F. Michael, A.J. Rubinstein, J.L. Mueller, C.S. Petersen, M.D. and Calais, E. (2015) 'Increasing Seismicity in the US Midcontinent: Implications for Earthquake Hazard,' *The Leading Edge*, 34(6): 618–626.

Espinosa, C. (2019) 'Interpretive Affinities: The Constitutionalization of Rights of Nature, Pacha Mama, in Ecuador,' *Journal of Environmental Policy & Planning*, 21(5): 608–622.

Essmann, H.F. Andrian, G. Pattenella, D. and Vantomme, P. (2007) 'Influence of Globalization on Forests and Forestry,' *Allgemeine Forest Und Jagdzeitung*, 178(4): 59–84.

Fawole, O.G. Cai, X.M. and MacKenzie, A.R. (2016) 'Gas Flaring and Resultant Air Pollution: A Review Focusing on Black Carbon,' *Environmental Pollution*, 216: 182–197.

Foley, R.A. and Lahr, M.M. (2015) 'Lithic Landscapes: Early Human Impact from Stone Tool Production on the Central Saharan Environment,' *PLoS One*, 10(3): e0116482.

Food and Agriculture Organization of the United Nations. (2015) *Global Forest Resource Assessment Country Report: Suriname* [Online]. Available at: www.fao.org/3/a-az343e.pdf (Accessed: 27th April 2020).

Fussey, P. and South, N. (2012) 'Heading Toward a New Criminogenic Climate: Climate Change, Political Economy and Environmental Security,' in: White, R. (ed) *Climate Change From a Criminological Perspective*. New York: Springer.

Gaarder, E. (2013) ‘Evading Responsibility for Green Harm: State-Corporate Exploitation of Race, Class, and Gender Inequality,’ in: South, N. and Brisman, A. (eds) *The Routledge International Handbook of Green Criminology*. Abingdon: Routledge.

Gagnon Thompson, S.C. and Burton, M.A. (1994) ‘Ecocentric and Anthropocentric Attitudes Toward the Environment,’ *Journal of Environmental Psychology*, 14(2): 149–157.

Garber, S.J. (2006) *Outer Space Treaty of 1967*. Produced for: NASA. Available at: https://history.nasa.gov/1967treaty.html (Accessed: 05th May 2020).

Gibbs, C. Gore, M.L. McGarrell, E.F. and Rivers III, L. (2010) ‘Introducing Conservation Criminology: Towards Interdisciplinary Scholarship on Environmental Crimes and Risks,’ *The British Journal of Criminology*, 50(1): 124–144.

Gore, M.L. (ed) (2017) *Conservation Criminology*. Chichester: John Wiley & Sons Ltd.

Goyes, D.R. and South, N. (2017) ‘Green Criminology Before “Green Criminology”: Amnesia and Absences,’ *Critical Criminology*, 25(2): 165–181.

Grear, A. Grant, E. Kerns, T. Morrow, K. and Short, D. (2014) *A Human Rights Assessment of Hydraulic Fracturing and Other Unconventional Gas Development in the United Kingdom*. Available at: https://uwe-repository.worktribe.com/output/824462/a-human-rights-assessment-of-hydraulic-fracturing-and-other-unconventional-gas-development-in-the-united-kingdom (Accessed: 25th November 2015).

Green, E.C. (1978) ‘Winti and Christianity: A Study in Religious Change,’ *Ethnohistory*, 25(3): 251–276.

Greene, H. (2011) ‘Cosmology and Earth Jurisprudence,’ in: Burdon, P.D. (ed) *Exploring Wild Law: The Philosophy of Earth Jurisprudence*. Mile End, Australia: Wakefield Press.

Greife, M.B. and Stretesky, P.B. (2013) ‘Crude Laws: Treadmill of Production and State Variations in Civil and Criminal Liability for Oil Discharges in Navigable Waters,’ in: South, N. and Brisman, A. (eds) *The Routledge International Handbook of Green Criminology*. Abingdon: Routledge.

Griffin, S. (1978) *Woman and Nature: The Roaring Inside Her*. New York: Harper and Row.

Gross, M. (2019) ‘Shrinking Ice Caps, Rising Oceans,’ *Current Biology*, 29(5): R137–R140.

Gupta, A. (2019) ‘Regulating Space Debris as Separate from Space Objects,’ *University of Pennsylvania Journal of International Law*, 41(1): 223–248.

Haley, A.G. (1958) ‘Law of Outer Space – A Problem for International Agreement,’ *American University Law Review*, 7: 70–77.

Hall, M. (2013) *Victims of Environmental Harm: Rights, Recognition and Redress Under National and International Law*. Abingdon: Routledge.

Halsey, M. (2013) ‘Conservation Criminology and the “General Accident” of Climate Change,’ in: South, N. and Brisman, A. (eds) *The Routledge International Handbook of Green Criminology*. Abingdon: Routledge.

Halsey, M. (2004) ‘Against “Green” Criminology,’ *British Journal of Criminology*, 44(6): 833–853.

Halsey, M. and White, R. (1998) 'Crime, Ecophilosophy and Environmental Harm,' *Theoretical Criminology*, 2(3): 345–371.

Harrison, J. (2017) *Saving the Oceans Through Law: The International Legal Framework for the Protection of the Marine Environment*. Oxford: Oxford University Press.

He, J. Yan, C. Holyoak, M. Wan, X. Ren, G. Hou, Y. Xie, Y. and Zhang, Z. (2018) 'Quantifying the Effects of Climate and Anthropogenic Change on Regional Species Loss in China,' *PLoS One*, 13(7): e0199735.

Hertzfeld, H.R. and Pace, S.N. (2013) 'Space Law: International Cooperation on Human Lunar Heritage,' *Science*, 342(6162): 1049–1050.

Heydon, J. (2019) *Sustainable Development as Environmental Harm: Rights, Regulation, and Injustice in the Canadian Oil Sands*. Abingdon: Routledge.

Heydon, J. (2018) 'Sensitising Green Criminology to Procedural Environmental Justice: A Case Study of First Nation Consultation in the Canadian Oil Sands,' *International Journal for Crime, Justice and Social Democracy*, 7(4): 67–82.

Higgins, P. Short, D. and South, N. (2013) 'Protecting the Planet: A Proposal for a Law of Ecocide,' *Crime, Law and Social Change*, 59(3): 251–266.

Hillyard, P. Pantazis, C. Tombs, S. and Gordon, D. (2004) *Beyond Criminology: Taking Harm Seriously*. London: Pluto Press.

Hillyard, P. and Tombs, S. (2017) 'Social Harm and Zemiology,' in: Liebling, A. Maruna, S. and McAra, L. (eds) *The Oxford Handbook of Criminology*. Oxford: Oxford University Press. 6th Edition.

Hirsch, J.K. Smalley, K.B. Selby-Nelson, E.M. Hamel-Lambert, J.M. Rosmann, M.R. Barnes, T.A. Abrahamson, D. Meit, S.S. Greywolf, I. Beckmann, S. and LaFromboise, T. (2017) 'Psychosocial Impact of Fracking: A Review of the Literature on the Mental Health Consequences of Hydraulic Fracturing,' *International Journal of Mental Health and Addiction*, 16: 1–15.

Hoffman, B. (2013) 'Exploring Biocultural Contexts: Comparative Woody Plant Knowledge of an Indigenous and Afro-American Maroon Community in Suriname, South America,' in: Voeks, R. and Rashford, J. (eds) *African Ethnobotany in the Americas*. New York: Springer.

Hosken, L. (2011) 'Reflections on an Inter-Cultural Journey into Earth Jurisprudence,' in: Burdon, P.D. (ed) *Exploring Wild Law: The Philosophy of Earth Jurisprudence*. Mile End, Australia: Wakefield Press.

Hsiao, E.C. (2012) 'Whanganui River Agreement,' *Environmental Policy and Law*, 42(6): 371–375.

Huang, M.N. (2017) 'Ecologies of Entanglement in the Great Pacific Garbage Patch,' *Journal of Asian American Studies*, 20(1): 95–117.

Hulsman, L.H.C. (1986) 'Critical Criminology and the Concept of Crime,' *Contemporary Crises*, 10(1): 63–83.

Humphreys, D. (2017) 'Rights of Pachamama: The Emergence of an Earth Jurisprudence in the Americas,' *Journal of International Relations and Development*, 20(3): 459–484.

Humphreys, D. (2015) 'Know Your Rights: Earth Jurisprudence and Environmental Politics,' *International Journal of Sustainability Policy and Practice*, 10(3–4): 1–14.

Jackson, R.B. Vengosh, A. Carey, J.W. Davies, R.J. Darrah, T.H. O'Sullivan, F. and Pétron, G. (2014) 'The Environmental Costs and Benefits of Fracking,' *Annual Review of Environment and Resources*, 39: 327–362.

Johnson, D.S. (2017) 'The Status of Green Criminology in Victimology Research,' *McNair Scholars Research Journal*, 10(1): 89–105.

Johnson, C.N. Balmford, A. Brook, B.W. Buettel, J.C. Galetti, M. Guangchun, L. and Wilmshurst, J.M. (2017) 'Biodiversity Losses and Conservation Responses in the Anthropocene,' *Science*, 356(6335): 270–275.

Katzenbach, N. (1958) 'Law and Lawyers in Space,' *Bulletin of the Atomic Scientists*, 14(6): 220–224.

Koons, J.E. (2012) 'At the Tipping Point: Defining an Earth Jurisprudence for Social and Ecological Justice,' *Loyola Law Review*, 58: 349–390.

Koons, J.E. (2011) 'Key Principles to Transform Law for the Health of the Planet,' in: Burdon, P.D. (ed) *Exploring Wild Law: The Philosophy of Earth Jurisprudence*. Mile End, Australia: Wakefield Press.

Koons, J.E. (2009) 'What Is Earth Jurisprudence: Key Principles to Transform Law for the Health of the Planet,' *Penn State Environmental Law Review*, 18: 47–68

Koons, J.E. (2008) 'Earth Jurisprudence: The Moral Value of Nature,' *Pace Environmental Law Review*, 25(2): 262–339.

Kramer, R.C. (2013) 'Carbon in the Atmosphere and Power in America: Climate Change as State-Corporate Crime,' *Journal of Crime and Justice*, 36(2): 153–170.

Kretser, H.E. Wong, R. Roberton, S. Pershyn, C. Huang, J. Sun, F. Kang, A. and Zahler, P. (2015) 'Mobile Decision-Tree Tool Technology as a Means to Detect Wildlife Crimes and Build Enforcement Networks,' *Biological Conservation*, 189: 33–38.

Lampkin, J.A. (2020a) 'The Uncertainty of Community Financial Incentives for "Fracking": Pursuing Ramifications for Environmental Justice,' in: Brisman, A. and South, N. (eds) *Routledge International Handbook of Green Criminology*. Abingdon: Routledge. 2nd Edition.

Lampkin, J.A. (2020b) 'Mapping the Terrain of an Astro-Green Criminology: A Case for Extending the Green Criminological Lens Outside of Planet Earth,' Under Review.

Lampkin, J.A. (2018) *Will Unconventional, Horizontal, Hydraulic Fracturing for Shale Gas Production Purposes Create Environmental Harm in the United Kingdom?* [PhD, University of Lincoln] [Online]. Available at: http://eprints.lincoln.ac.uk/id/eprint/35711/1/Jack%20Lampkin%20PhD%20Thesis.pdf (Accessed: 25th March 2020).

Lampkin, J.A. (2016) 'Green Criminology and Fracking in the UK: An Application of Utilitarian Ethics,' *Papers from the British Society of Criminology Conference*, 16(2): 20–37. [Online]. Available at: www.britsoccrim.org/wpcontent/uploads/2016/12/pbcc_2016_lampkin.pdf (Accessed: 23rd May 2018).

Lampkin, J.A. and Wyatt, T. (2019) 'Utilising Principles of Earth Jurisprudence to Prevent Environmental Harm: Applying a Case Study of Unconventional Hydraulic Fracturing for Shale Gas in the United Kingdom,' *Critical Criminology*: 1–16. [Online]. Available at: https://doi.org/10.1007/s10612-018-9426-7 (Accessed: 01st April 2020).

Latawiec, A.E. Strassburg, B.B. Rodriguez, A.M. Matt, E. Nijbroek, R. and Silos, M. (2014) 'Suriname: Reconciling Agricultural Development and Conservation of Unique Natural Wealth,' *Land Use Policy*, 38: 627–636.

Lebreton, L. Slat, B. Ferrari, F. Sainte-Rose, B. Aitken, J. Marthouse, R. Hajbane, S. Cunsolo, S. Schwarz, A. Levivier, A. and Noble, K. (2018) 'Evidence That the Great Pacific Garbage Patch Is Rapidly Accumulating Plastic,' *Scientific Reports*, 8(1): 1–15.

Lewis, S.L. and Maslin, M.A. (2015) 'Defining the Anthropocene,' *Nature*, 519: 171–180.

Loder, R.E. (2018) 'Asteroid Mining: Ecological Jurisprudence Beyond Earth,' *Virginia Environmental Law Journal*, 36(3): 275–317.

Lynch, M.J. (2014) *Gaia Theory* [Online]. Available at: http://greencriminology.org/glossary/gaia-theory/ (Accessed: 30th April 2020).

Lynch, M.J. (1990) 'The Greening of Criminology: A Perspective on the 1990's,' *The Critical Criminologist*, 2(3): 1–4 and 11–12.

Lynch, M.J. Barrett, K.L. Stretesky, P.B. and Long, M.A. (2017) 'The Neglect of Quantitative Research in Green Criminology and Its Consequences,' *Critical Criminology*, 25(2): 183–198.

Lynch, M.J. Long, M.A. Barrett, K.L. and Stretesky, P.B. (2013) 'Is It a Crime to Produce Ecological Disorganization? Why Green Criminology and Political Economy Matter in the Analysis of Global Ecological Harms,' *British Journal of Criminology*, 53(6): 997–1016.

Lynch, M.J. Long, M.A. and Stretesky, P.B. (2019) *Green Criminology and Green Theories of Justice: An Introduction to a Political Economic View of Eco-Justice*. London: Palgrave Studies in Green Criminology.

Lynch, M.J. and Pires, S.F. (eds) (2019) *Quantitative Studies in Green and Conservation Criminology: The Measurement of Environmental Harm and Crime*. New York: Routledge.

Lynch, M.J. and Stretesky, P.B. (2014) *Exploring Green Criminology: Toward a Green Criminological Revolution*. Burlington: Ashgate Publishing Limited.

Lynch, M.J. and Stretesky, P.B. (2003) 'The Meaning of Green: Towards a Clarification of the Term Green and Its Meaning for the Development of a Green Criminology,' *Theoretical Criminology*, 7(2): 217–238.

Maher, J. and Wyatt, T. (2017) 'International Trade in Animals and Animal Parts,' in: Maher, J. Pierpoint, H. and Beirne, P. (eds) *The Palgrave International Handbook of Animal Abuse Studies*. London: Palgrave Macmillan.

Maloney, M. and Siemen, P. (2015) 'Responding to the Great Work: The Role of Earth Jurisprudence and Wild Law in the 21st Century,' *Earth Jurisprudence and Environmental Justice Journal*, 5: 6–22.

Mason, I. (2011) 'Exploring Wild Law,' in: Burdon, P.D. (ed) *Exploring Wild Law: The Philosophy of Earth Jurisprudence*. Mile End, Australia: Wakefield Press.

Matheny, G. (2006) 'Utilitarianism and Animals,' in: Singer, P. (ed) *In Defense of Animals: The Second Wave*. Malden: Blackwell Publishing Limited.

Matthews, J.J. and McMahon, S. (2018) 'Exogeoconservation: Protecting Geological Heritage on Celestial Bodies,' *Acta Astronautica*, 149: 55–60.

McClanahan, B. (2014) 'Green and Grey: Water Justice, Criminalization, and Resistance,' *Critical Criminology*, 22: 403–418.

McGrory Klyza, C. (1994) 'Do Trees Have Rights? Rights, Nature, and Conceptual Change,' *Southeastern Political Review*, 22: 425–444.

Merchant, C. (1990) 'Environmental Ethics and Political Conflict,' *Environmental Ethics*, 12(1): 45–68.

Muehlenbachs, L. Spiller, E. and Timmins, C. (2015) *The Housing Market Impacts of Shale Gas Development: Working Paper 19796*. Produced for: National Bureau of Economic Research [Online]. Available at: www.nber.org/papers/w19796.pdf (Accessed: 05th May 2020).

Murray, J. (2015) 'Earth Jurisprudence, Wild Law, Emergent Law: The Emerging Field of Ecology and Law – Part 2,' *Liverpool Law Review*, 36: 105–122.

Nash, R.F. (1989) *The Rights of Nature: A History of Environmental Ethics*. London: The University of Wisconsin Press.

Newburn, T. (2007) *Criminology*. Cullompton: Willan Publishing.

Nurse, A. (2015) *Policing Wildlife: Perspectives on the Enforcement of Wildlife Legislation*. London: Palgrave Studies in Green Criminology.

Nurse, A. (2013) 'Species Justice: The Future Protection of Wildlife and the Reform of Wildlife Laws,' *The Green Criminology Monthly*, 2013(6): 1–11.

The Ocean Cleanup. (2020) *Oceans: Cleaning Up the Garbage Patches* [Online]. Available at: https://theoceancleanup.com/oceans/ (Accessed: 10th April 2020).

O'Donnell, E.L. (2018) 'At the Intersection of the Sacred and the Legal: Rights for Nature in Uttarakhand, India,' *Journal of Environmental Law*, 30(1): 135–144.

O'Donnell, M.C. Gilfillan, S.M.V. Edlmann, K. and McDermott, C.I. (2018) 'Wastewater from Hydraulic Fracturing in the UK: Assessing the Viability and Cost of Management,' *Environmental Science: Water Research and Technology*, 4(2): 325–335.

O'Donoghue, P. and Rutz, C. (2016) 'Real-Time Anti-Poaching Tags Could Help Prevent Imminent Species Extinctions,' *Journal of Applied Ecology*, 53: 5–10.

Parker, C. and Johnson, H. (2019) 'From Food Chains to Food Webs: Regulating Capitalist Production and Consumption in the Food System,' *Annual Review of Law and Social Science*, 15: 205–225.

Pepper, D. (1993) *Eco-Socialism: From Deep Ecology to Social Justice*. Abingdon: Routledge.

Pimm, S.L. and Raven, P.H. (2017) 'The Fate of the World's Plants,' *Trends in Ecology and Evolution*, 32(5): 317–320.

Potter, G.R. (2013) 'Justifying 'Green' Criminology: Values and 'Taking Sides' in an Ecologically Informed Social Science,' in: Cowburn, M. Duggan, M. Robinson, A. and Senior, P. (eds) *Values in Criminology and Community Justice*. Bristol: Policy Press.

Prud'homme, A. (2014) *Hydrofracking: What Everyone Needs to Know*. New York: Oxford University Press.

Quinn, A.G. (2008) 'The New Age of Space Law: The Outer Space Treaty and the Weaponization of Space,' *Minnesota Journal of International Law*, 17(2): 475–502.

Raihan, A. Begum, R.A. Said, M. Nizam, M. and Abdullah, S.M.S. (2019) 'A Review of Emission Reduction Potential and Cost Savings Through Forest Carbon Sequestration,' *Asian Journal of Water, Environment and Pollution*, 16(3): 1–7.

Ramirez-Gomez, S.O. (2011) *Spatial Drivers of Deforestation in Suriname*. Produced for: The Center for Agriculture Research in Suriname, Tropenbos Suriname [Online]. Available at: http://forestindustries.eu/sites/default/files/userfiles/1file/sara_suriname.pdf (Accessed: 27th April 2020).

Redd+ Suriname. (2020) *Suriname Is the Most Forested Country in the World, Why Would a Forest Protection Program Still Be Necessary*? [Online]. Available at: www.surinameredd.org/en/reddplus-suriname/ (Accessed: 28th April 2020).

Rinaldi, R. (2015) 'Fracturing the Keystone: Why Fracking in Pennsylvania Should Be Considered an Abnormally Dangerous Activity,' *Widener Law Journal*, 24: 385–432.

Rogers, N. (2017) 'Performance and Pedagogy in the Wild Law Judgment Project,' *Legal Education Review*, 27(1): 1–19.

Román-Palacios, C. and Wiens, J.J. (2020) 'Recent Responses to Climate Change Reveal the Drivers of Species Extinction and Survival,' *Proceedings of the National Academy of Sciences*, 117(8): 4211–4217.

Roopsind, A. Sohngen, B. and Brandt, J. (2019) 'Evidence That a National REDD+ Program Reduces Tree Cover Loss and Carbon Emissions in a High Forest Cover, Low Deforestation Country,' *Proceedings of the National Academy of Sciences*, 116(49): 24492–24499.

Rowe, B.D. (2011) 'Understanding Animals-Becoming-Meat: Embracing a Disturbing Education,' *Critical Education*, 2(7): 1–25 [Online]. Available at: http://m1.cust.educ.ubc.ca/journal/index.php/criticaled/article/view/132 (Accessed: 06th May 2020).

Rowe, T. (2019) 'The Fight for Ancestral Rivers: A Study of the Maori and the Legal Personhood Status of the Whanganui River and Whether Maori Strategies Can Be Used to Preserve the Menominee River,' *Michigan State International Law Review*, 27(3): 593–627.

Ruddell, R. (2017) *Oil, Gas and Crime: The Dark Side of the Boom*. New York: Palgrave Macmillan.

Ruggiero, V. and South, N. (2013) 'Green Criminology and Crimes of the Economy: Theory, Research and Praxis,' *Critical Criminology*, 21(3): 359–373.

Rühs, N. and Jones, A. (2016) 'The Implementation of Earth Jurisprudence Through Substantive Constitutional Rights of Nature,' *Sustainability*, 8(2): 174–193.

Samaan, A.W. (2011) 'Enforcement of International Environmental Treaties: An Analysis,' *Fordham Environmental Law Journal*, 5(1): 261–283.

Saunders, P.J. McCoy, D. Goldstein, R. Saunders, A.T. and Munroe, A. (2018) 'A Review of the Public Health Impacts of Unconventional Natural Gas Development,' *Environmental Geochemistry and Health*, 40(1): 1–57.

Schierhorn, F. Meyfroidt, P. Kastner, T. Kuemmerle, T. Prishchepov, A.V. and Müller, D. (2016) 'The Dynamics of Beef Trade Between Brazil and Russia and Their Environmental Implications,' *Global Food Security*, 11: 84–92.

Schillmoller, A. and Pelizzon, A. (2013) 'Mapping the Terrain of Earth Jurisprudence: Landscape, Thresholds and Horizons,' *Environment and Earth Law Journal*, 3: 1–32.

Sebastian, M. (2017) 'Deadly Efficiency: The Impact of Capitalist Production on the "Meat" Industry, Slaughterhouse Workers, and Nonhuman Animals,' in: Nibert, D. (ed) *Animal Oppression and Capitalism. Volume 1: The Oppression of Animals as Sources of Food*. Santa Barbara, CA: Praeger.

Shearing, C. (2015) 'Criminology and the Anthropocene,' *Criminology and Criminal Justice*, 15(3): 255–269.
Short, D. (2020) 'Energy Harms, "Extreme Energy," Fracking and Water,' in: Brisman, A. and South, N. (eds) *Routledge International Handbook of Green Criminology*. Abingdon: Routledge. 2nd Edition.
Short, D. Elliot, J. Norder, K. Lloyd-Davies, E. and Morley, J. (2015) 'Extreme Energy, "Fracking" and Human Rights: A New Field for Human Rights Impact Assessments?' *The International Journal of Human Rights*, 19(6): 697–736.
Situ, Y. and Emmons, D. (2000) *Criminal Law and the Environment*. Thousand Oaks: Sage.
Sollund, R.A. (2015) 'Introduction: Critical Green Criminology – An Agenda for Change,' in: Sollund, R.A. (ed) *Green Harms and Crimes*. London: Palgrave Macmillan.
Sollund, R.A. (2013) 'The Victimization of Women, Children and Non-Human Species Through Trafficking and Trade: Crimes Understood Through an Ecofeminist Perspective,' in: South, N. and Brisman, A. (eds) *Routledge International Handbook of Green Criminology*. Abingdon: Routledge.
South, N. (2015) 'Anticipating the Anthropocene and Greening Criminology,' *Criminology and Criminal Justice*, 15(3): 270–276.
South, N. (2014) 'Green Criminology: Reflections, Connections, Horizons,' *International Journal for Crime, Justice and Social Democracy*, 3(2): 5–20.
South, N. (1998) 'A Green Field for Criminology? A Proposal for a Perspective,' *Theoretical Criminology*, 2(2): 211–233.
South, N. and Brisman, A. (2012) 'Critical Green Criminology, Environmental Rights and Crimes of Exploitation,' in: Winlow, S. and Atkinson, R. (eds) *New Directions in Crime and Deviancy*. Abingdon: Routledge.
South, N. Brisman, A. and Beirne, P. (2013) 'A Guide to a Green Criminology,' in: South, N. and Brisman, A. (eds) *Routledge International Handbook of Green Criminology*. Abingdon: Routledge.
Speight, J.G. (2013) *Shale Gas Production Processes*. Oxford: Elsevier.
Spencer, D.C. and Fitzgerald, A. (2013) 'Three Ecologies, Transversality and Victimization: The Case of the British Petroleum Oil Spill,' *Crime, Law and Social Change*, 59(2): 209–223.
Sterba, J.P. (2011) 'Biocentrism Defended,' *Ethics, Policy & Environment*, 14(2): 167–169.
Stretesky, P.B. Long, M.A. and Lynch, M.J. (2014) *The Treadmill of Crime: Political Economy and Green Criminology*. New York: Routledge.
Stretesky, P.B. and Lynch, M.J. (1998) 'Corporate Environmental Violence and Racism,' *Crime, Law and Social Change*, 30(2): 163–184.
Stretesky, P.B. and McKie, R. (2016) 'A Perspective on the Historical Analysis of Race and Treatment Storage and Disposal Facilities in the United States,' *Environmental Research Letters*, 11(3): 1–3. [Online]. Available at: http://doi.org/10.1088/1748-9326/11/3/031001 (Accessed: 02nd April 2020).
Takemura, N. (2019) 'Astro-Green Criminology: A New Perspective Against Space Capitalism Outer Space Mining May Make the Same Mistakes in Space as We

Have on Earth,' *Toin University of Yokohama Research Bulletin* (40 – June 2019): 7–17 [Online]. Available at: https://irdb.nii.ac.jp/en/00913/0004060669 (Accessed: 20th April 2020).

Tapia-Armijos, M.F. Homeier, J. Espinosa, C.I. Leuschner, C. and de la Cruz, M. (2015) 'Deforestation and Forest Fragmentation in South Ecuador Since the 1970s – Losing a Hotspot of Biodiversity,' *PLoS One*, 10(9): 1–18.

Turner, S.J. (2013a) *A Global Environmental Right*. Abingdon: Routledge.

Turner, S.J. (2013b) 'Factors in the Development of a Global Substantive Environmental Right,' *Oñati Socio-Legal Series*, 3(5): 893–907.

Van Andel, T. (2010) 'How African-Based Winti Belief Helps to Protect Forests in Suriname,' in: Verschurren, B. Wild, R. McNeely, J. and Oviedo, G. (eds) *Sacred Natural Sites: Conserving Nature and Culture*. London: Earthscan.

Van Andel, T. and Havinga, R. (2008) 'Sustainability Aspects of Commercial Medicinal Plant Harvesting in Suriname,' *Forest Ecology and Management*, 256(8): 1540–1545.

Van der Werf, G.R. Morton, D.C. DeFries, R.S. Olivier, J.G. Kasibhatla, P.S. Jackson, R.B. Collatz, G.J. and Randerson, J.T. (2009) 'CO2 Emissions from Forest Loss,' *Nature Geoscience*, 2(11): 737–738.

Van Oosterzee, P. Blignaut, J. and Bradshaw, C.J.A. (2012) 'iREDD Hedges Against Avoided Deforestation's Unholy Trinity of Leakage, Permanence and Additionality,' *Conservation Letters*, 5(4): 266–273.

Van Rossum, M.K. (2017) *The Green Amendment: Securing Our Rights to a Healthy Environment*. New York: Disruption Books.

Van Uhm, D. and Siegel, D. (2016) 'The Illegal Trade in Black Caviar,' *Trends in Organized Crime*, 19(1): 67–87.

Wabnitz, C. and Nichols, W.J. (2010) 'Plastic Pollution: An Ocean Emergency,' *Marine Turtle Newsletter*, 129: 1–4.

Walklate, S. (2005) *Criminology: The Basics*. Abingdon: Routledge.

Walters, R. (2013) 'Air Crimes and Atmospheric Justice,' in: South, N. and Brisman, A. (eds) *Routledge International Handbook of Green Criminology*. Abingdon: Routledge.

Walters, R. (2010) 'Eco Crime,' in: Muncie, J. Talbot, D. and Walters, R. (eds) *Crime: Local and Global*. Cullompton: Willan.

Watson, R.A. (1983) 'A Critique of Anti-Anthropocentric Biocentrism,' *Environmental Ethics*, 5(3): 245–256.

Wells, H.G. (1898) *The War of the Worlds*. London: Collins Classics. Edition Published in 2017.

Werger, M.J.A. (ed) (2011) *Sustainable Management of Tropical Rainforests: The CELOS Management System*. Published by: Tropenbos International, Parimaribo, Suriname. Series 25 [Online]. Available at: https://library.wur.nl/WebQuery/wur pubs/421543 (Accessed: 05th May 2020).

Westra, L. (2009) *Environmental Justice and the Rights of Ecological Refugees*. Abingdon: Routledge.

Weyer, F. (2019) 'Implementing "Vivir Bien": Results and Lessons from the Biocultural Programme, Bolivia,' in: Carbonnier, G. Campodónico, H. and

Vázquez, S.T. (eds) *Alternative Pathways to Sustainable Development: Lessons from Latin America*. Leiden: Brill Nijhoff.

White, R. (2019) 'Green Criminology,' in: McLaughlin, E. and Muncie, J. (eds) *The Sage Dictionary of Criminology*. London: Sage Publications Ltd. 4th Edition.

White, R. (2018) *Climate Change Criminology*. Bristol: Bristol University Press.

White, R. (2013a) *Environmental Harm: An Eco-Justice Perspective*. Bristol: Policy Press.

White, R. (2013b) 'The Conceptual Contours of Green Criminology,' in: Walters, R. Westerhuis, D.S. and Wyatt, T. (eds) *Emerging Issues in Green Criminology*. London: Palgrave Macmillan.

White, R. (2010) 'Globalisation and Environmental Harm,' in: White, R. (ed) *Global Environmental Harm: Criminological Perspectives*. Cullompton: Willan.

White, R. (2008a) *Crimes Against Nature: Environmental Criminology and Ecological Justice*. New York: Willan Publishing.

White, R. (2008b) 'Environmental Harm and Crime Prevention,' *Trends and Issues in Crime and Criminal Justice*, 360: 1–6.

White, R. (2005) 'Environmental Crime in Global Context: Exploring the Theoretical and Empirical Complexities,' *Current Issues in Criminal Justice*, 16(3): 271–285.

Williams, M. (2003) *Deforesting the Earth: From Prehistory to Global Crisis*. London: The University of Chicago Press.

Wiseman, H.J. (2011) 'Trade Secrets, Disclosure, and Dissent in a Fracturing Energy Revolution,' *Columbia Law Review*, 111: 1–13.

Wolfgang, M.E. (1963) 'Criminology and the Criminologist,' *Criminal Law, Criminology & Police Science*, 54(2): 155–162.

Woods, K. (2006) 'What Does the Language of Human Rights Bring to Campaigns for Environmental Justice?' *Environmental Politics*, 15(4): 572–591.

Worm, B. Barbier, E.B. Beaumont, N. Duffy, J.E. Folke, C. Halpern, B.S. Jackson, J.B. Lotze, H.K. Micheli, F. Palumbi, S.R. and Sala, E. (2006) 'Impacts of Biodiversity Loss on Ocean Ecosystem Services,' *Science*, 314(5800): 787–790.

Wright, G. (2013) 'Climate Regulation as If the Planet Matters: The Earth Jurisprudence Approach to Climate Change,' *Environmental and Earth Law Journal*, 3(1): 33–57.

Wyatt, T. (2013) *Wildlife Trafficking: A Deconstruction of the Crime, the Victims and the Offenders*. London: Palgrave.

Wyatt, T. (2009) 'Exploring the Organization of Russia Far East's Illegal Wildlife Trade: Two Case Studies of the Illegal Fur and Illegal Falcon Trades,' *Global* Crime, 10(1–2): 144–154.

Yurimoto, H. Abe, K.I. Abe, M. Ebihara, M. Fujimura, A. Hashiguchi, M. Hashizume, K. Ireland, T.R. Itoh, S. Katayama, J. Kato, C. Kawaguchi, J. Kawasaki, N. Kitajima, F. Kobayashi, S. Meike, T. Mukai, T. Nagao, K. Nakamura, T. Naraoka, H. Noguchi, T. Okazaki, R. Park, C. Sakamoto, N. Seto, Y. Takei, M. Tsuchiyama, A. Uesugi, M. Wakaki, S. Yada, T. Yamamoto, K. Yoshikawa, M. and Zolensky, M.E. (2011) 'Oxygen Isotopic Compositions of Asteroidal Materials Returned from Itokawa by the Hayabusa Mission,' *Science*, 333: 1116–1119.

Zaiton, S. Paridah, M. Hazandy, A. and Azim, R.A.R.A. (2018) 'Potential of Eucalyptus Plantation in Malaysia,' *The Malaysian Forester*, 81(1): 64–72.
Zalaseiwicz, J. Williams, M. Stefen, W. and Crutzen, P. (2010) 'The New World of the Anthropocene,' *Environmental Science and Technology*, 44: 2228–2231.
Zalman, J. Ellis, P.W. Crabbe, S. and Roopsind, A. (2019) 'Opportunities for Carbon Emissions Reduction from Selective Logging in Suriname,' *Forest Ecology and Management*, 439: 9–17.
Zijlstra, S. (2014) 'Competing for European Settlers: Local Loyalties of Colonial Governments in Suriname and Jamaica, 1660–1680,' *Journal of Early American History*, 4(2): 149–166.

Index

Note: Page numbers in **bold** indicate a table on the corresponding page.

BW - #0004 - 210622 - C0 - 216/138/7 - PB - 9780367613112 - Gloss Lamination